WORKSHOP
OF THE WORLD

BIRMINGHAM'S
INDUSTRIAL LEGACY

RAY SHILL

First published in 2006 by
Sutton Publishing Limited · Phoenix Mill
Thrupp · Stroud · Gloucestershire · GL5 2BU

British Library Cataloguing in Publication Data
A catalogue record for this book is available from the British Library

ISBN 0-7509-3503-0

ACKNOWLEDGEMENTS

Special thanks must go to the staff of Birmingham Public Libraries (Archives, Local Studies), The National Archives (Public Record Office), Warwickshire Record Office, and to Hudson's Whistles, Llewellyn Ryland and Kappa SSK.

Typeset in 10.5/12.5 Garamond
Typesetting and origination by
Sutton Publishing Limited.
Printed and bound in England by
J.H. Haynes & Co. Ltd, Sparkford.

CONTENTS

INTRODUCTION

The inventiveness of Birmingham manufacturers was quite remarkable. Their ability to take on new products and adopt modern methods enabled the introduction of a wide range of different trades and established Birmingham as an important manufacturing centre. They were fortunate to be able to draw on the skills of local people, whose assistance was essential to the continued success of any company. Many firms showed versatility and the ability to adapt and pursue lucrative lines and there was a ready market for their products not only in Britain but also throughout the British Empire and indeed the world. It was no small wonder that when the British Association held their Exhibition in Birmingham in 1886, they credited Birmingham as the Workshop of the World.

Specialist crafts were interwoven with metal fashioning abilities that were to be found in Birmingham and surrounding communities located in the Black Country, Coventry and Redditch. Metal working has remained an important skill through to the present day. The methods might have changed, as have the tools and machines and techniques needed to accomplish the task. Yet metal fashioning is needed as much today as it ever has been.

The first forms of mechanical power entailed the use of water- and wind-powered mills. Water power, in particular, proved invaluable to the development of local industry. The rivers local to the Birmingham district were the Cole, Rea and Tame. They provided a natural, but hard-won power source. Watermills were arranged at strategic places alongside these rivers or the streams and brooks that fed them. A common method was to build up a head of water behind a dam and divert the surplus flow around through a series of man-made channels, called races.

Watermills played important roles in the industrial revolution. Mills were used to grind corn into flour, but their wheels could also be used for industrial work such as rolling metal or grinding edge tools. Some were also adapted to provide the blast for smelting iron, forging iron or pounding rags for paper making. Watermills were a constant feature of Birmingham industry through to the early years of the twentieth century. Perhaps the most famous local watermill is Sarehole Mill, which was a corn mill built in the 1760s that worked through to 1919. It is well known because of its association with the author J.R.R. Tolkien.

Working with water had its drawbacks as supply was sometimes restricted and power of the mill was equally limited to the turning of the wheel, or wheels. The advent of the steam engine enabled factories to move away from the riverside and into the towns. Steam power did much to enhance the development of industry in Birmingham. Steam was a much more versatile means of driving machinery than the water mill. Engines could be placed close to the work and factory bosses were keen to exploit every new refinement in steam-engine technology. A feature of many nineteenth-century factories was the overhead or underfloor shafting that drove belting to dynamos, lathes and other machinery. Gas engines and oil engines added to the versatility of the power. But the most drastic change came through the adoption of electric power, which promoted the use of compact machinery and heavier presses.

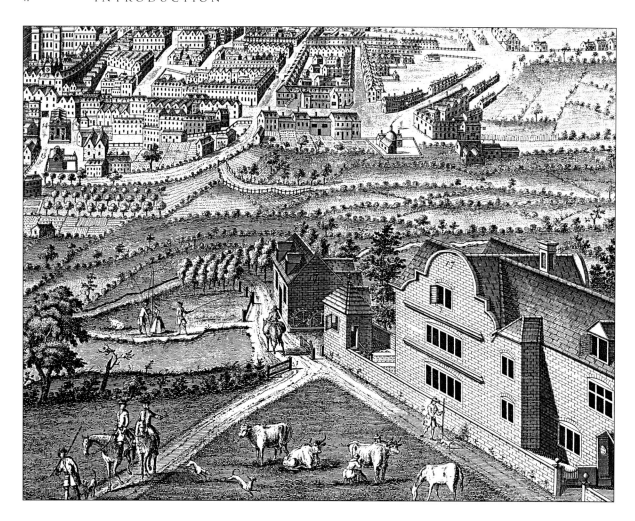

In the eighteenth century various prospect views of Birmingham were published. The South East Prospect included the Heath (or Cooper's) Mill, at Digbeth, which is shown in the centre of the enlarged section of the engraving. Heath Mill stood on the River Rea and used its waters to drive the water wheel. Water supply was controlled by floodgates that were aligned at the junction of the old river and the diverted course, which ran around the west side of the mill. The house (no. 17) belonged to Mr Cooper, the mill owner, while the two horsemen in the foreground are seen on Heath Mill Lane. (*Local Studies Department, Birmingham Reference Library*)

Right: Birmingham is a town of hills and valleys. This feature was used to best advantage by the windmill builders. Although the Birmingham windmills have long since gone, Windmill Street, Holloway Head, is a reminder of Chapman's Windmill, which formerly stood on the hillside nearby. This drawing of the Dog and Duck shows the windmill to the rear. (*Birmingham Weekly Mercury, October 20 1895*)

OUR ARTIST RECALLS

OLD BIRMINGHAM.

(COPYRIGHT.)

NO. 19.—THE "DOG AND DUCK," HOLLOWAY HEAD.

Tolkien drew his inspiration for his books from a variety of sources that included his childhood homes in Birmingham. Many other authors have also based fictional accounts around life in nineteenth- and twentieth-century Birmingham. There remains a host of untold stories and untold lives hidden in the rich industrial heritage of the district. Intertwined with the hard-working lives of many Birmingham people were the difficult working conditions that were common in the industrial towns and cities throughout Britain. Hardship had no boundaries whether people laboured in the factories and foundries of Birmingham, the mills of Manchester or the coalmines around Newcastle. Some employers, like Cadbury Brothers, adopted a benevolent attitude to their workers. The move from the smoke- and soot-laden atmosphere that prevailed around the city centre to the clean air and new factory site at Bournville was a caring move. Other factory owners shared similar views and made every attempt to improve the lot of their workers. Others did not. Workers' pay was often low and employment sometimes irregular. There were those who even lived in poverty. Such people were caught in the trap where income barely paid for rent and pawned belongings were the only financial buffer for food.

Yet new industry continued to draw skilled and unskilled workers to the city. From their numbers was derived an entrepreneurial spirit where workers used their abilities to adapt and found further trades. Birmingham at this time supported a large number of small industries and a proportionate small workforce. It was only during the twentieth century that company mergers and takeovers created the large workforce employers. Family-run firms were particularly common where father and sons built up the business.

The simple hand press was the universal tool of many small firms. The basic concept of pressing parts by hand was used to best advantage by the button, gun and steel pen nib makers.
(Birmingham Daily Post)

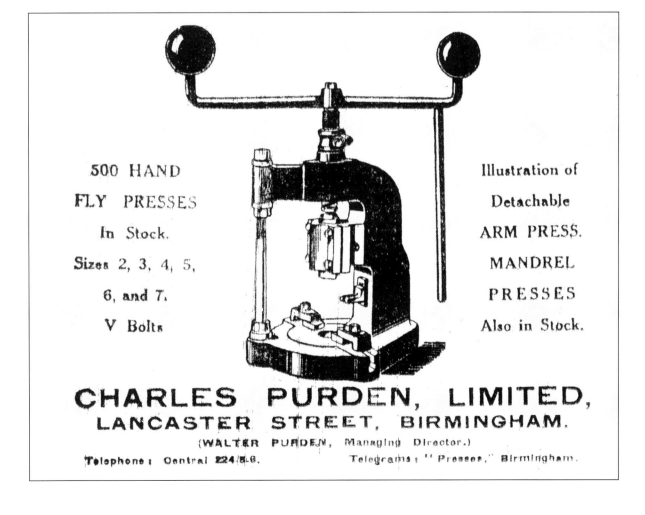

500 HAND
FLY PRESSES
In Stock.
Sizes 2, 3, 4, 5,
6, and 7.
V Bolts

Illustration of
Detachable
ARM PRESS.
MANDREL
PRESSES
Also in Stock.

CHARLES PURDEN, LIMITED,
LANCASTER STREET, BIRMINGHAM.
(WALTER PURDEN, Managing Director.)
Telephone: Central 224/5-6.   Telegrams: "Presses," Birmingham.

Time and again this pattern is repeated, and some went on to found large concerns. The names of Matthew Boulton and James Watt are frequently connected with the Birmingham engineering industry and their names head a long list of industrialists that were based in the town. Writers and historians have long praised Boulton and Watt as the industrial heroes that set Birmingham to commercial success, but there are many more who deserve a share of the credit and among their numbers the following deserve mention:

Herbert Austin, a pioneer of the automobile industry, set up the Longbridge Car Plant, where motor cars, commercial vehicles and aeroplanes were manufactured.

James Booth, engaged in the manufacture of Duralumin alloys, which assisted the manufacture of aircraft components.

Thomas Carlyle found fortune and success through the making of buttons.

Arthur Chamberlain may have been overshadowed by the political achievements of his brother, Joseph, but was a successful industrialist who turned around the fortunes of Kynochs. The firm founded by George Kynoch went on to be the keystone of the vast Imperial Metal Industries.

Benjamin Cook started as a jeweller and maker of steel toys, but then expanded his business to include the making of ornamental brassware and the first Birmingham-made metallic bedsteads.

Edward and Harry Crane set up a small bicycle-making business that developed into the massive Hercules Cycle Works in Aston.

Dudley, Ludford and William Docker started as retailers of black varnish and went on to manufacture varnishes and paints for automobiles, rail and road vehicles.

George and Henry Elkington brought the principles of electroplating to Birmingham and were integral to the foundation and development of this industry.

Henry Fulford brought new practice to the local brewery trade. Fulford was one of a number of brewers who established successful concerns and a pioneer in the use of up-to-date brewing methods at the Holt Brewery.

Joseph Gillott founded a successful business based on the making of steel pen nibs.

George Kynoch founded a business based on the making of percussion caps, that grew into a diverse group of occupations that included ammunition manufacture, metal working, cycle manufacture and soap-making.

Joseph Lucas began making oil lamps. He and his sons went on to found a multinational company that supplied parts to the automobile and aerospace industries.

Josiah Mason was a notable Birmingham entrepreneur who became a successful steel pen nib maker and was later a pioneer in the electroplate trade.

Alfred Morcam adapted his engineering skills to transform the business of G.E. Bellis into a successful marine engine and steam turbine manufacturing concern.

James Lansdown Norton started in business as a bicycle component maker during 1898 but went on to supply motors for bicycles and develop new motorcycles. He was the founder of Norton Motor Co., which gained an international reputation for the motorcycles produced at the Bracebridge Street factory.

William Priest helped to build up the reputation of the Quadrant Cycle Co. as a leading maker of quality bicycles and motorcycles.

Richard Prosser trained as a brass worker but studied engineering in his spare time. His work with tube manufacture helped to lay the foundation of the weldless tube industry.

John and Edmund Sturge came from Bewdley to establish a chemical works that produced citric acid and pure calcium carbonate.

James Webster came from Nottingham to work in Birmingham as an engineer and inventor. He devised an anti-fouling metallic paint, a method of steel making and a chemical means of extracting aluminium metal. His factory at Solihull Lodge was among the first in Britain to produce aluminium commercially.

Robert Walter Winfield founded an important brass foundry business that made gas fittings and ornamental brass work. He also deserves a share of the credit for the establishment of the metallic bedstead business in Birmingham.

John Wright came to Birmingham from his native Essex to found a gas stove business.

The nineteenth century proved important times for Birmingham industry. Out of the crucible of innovation came a host of new trades, which were developed alongside established business. Labour was constantly being drawn into the town from all parts of the country, bringing valued working skills with it.

In good or bad times, these people formed the reservoir for the many skills required to keep the wheels of industry in motion. There was a select group of common processes, which were adapted to suit the manufacturing trades. Many were related to the metal trades, where both ferrous and non-ferrous metals were worked into useful products. Any metal working begins with the basic metal, which was supplied to be worked up.

Some metals, such as iron, were brought from the blast furnace to the foundry where the skills of the caster, moulder and pattern maker were employed to produce a rough casting. Metals were also mixed together to produce a particular alloy. Bronze and the many types of brass were produced at the foundry according to the finely honed skill of the caster's art. A common aspect of Birmingham trade was for one place to make a rough article and another to take that article and finish it for a particular use.

In another part of the trade ingots of metal such as aluminium, brass, iron, nickel, phosphor bronze and steel were worked up by the extrusion machines and rolling mills to make bars, hoops, rails, sheets, tubes or wire. These, in turn, were worked up further by pressing, stamping, machining or lathe work into specific products that included buttons, buckles, nails and screws.

Charles Purden Ltd factory, Lancaster Street. *(Birmingham Daily Post)*

Through the working of iron lay the building blocks of a host of different industries. These ranged from cast holloware to the precision castings needed for the engineering trades. Foundries produced the shapes for others to work on and refine through hand filing, lathe work and drilling to the end product. Another method lay in the hands of the drop-forger, who through heat and hammering instilled strength into the metal.

Another aspect of metal work was the shaping and forming of metals by the die stamp and the press. Die stamping had a particular use in medal and medallion manufacture, but later came to be employed for the making of parts for the automotive and electrical industries. The humble hand press fulfilled many roles and was a familiar sight in the many workshops and factories across the city. Its uses ranged from stamping out pen nibs to making buttons. Some metals were easier to work up into a final product. Tin was brought into Birmingham for plating goods, but was also fashioned in finished articles known as pewter. Beer engine makers and bar fitters used pewter components.

Heavy press work became an important Birmingham trade through the scientific application of hydraulic and later electrical engineering. Presses were capable of shaping and forming sheets of iron and steel that proved so necessary to car and commercial vehicle manufacture. The making of domestic appliances and railway rolling stock construction came to prominence in twentieth-century Birmingham and is still a staple trade.

A worker at a rolling mill. *(Heartland Press Collection)*

George Morgan became noted among the Birmingham firms for quality forging for the car trade and was long associated with the Selly Oak factory that came to bear his name. He belonged to a select group of local businessmen who worked their way up to the level of company ownership. Components Ltd first employed George in 1910, when they were associated with the manufacture of cycle components and motor-cycles at the Dale Road Works. The group of factories in Dale Road included the Ariel Cycle Works and the Midland Tube and Forging Co. George Morgan became general manager for the tube works in 1919 and was still there as manager when, in 1926, the works became known as the Midland Forging Co. Ltd. They remained a Components Ltd subsidiary until 1932, when reorganisation separated the interests of Midland Forging and the Ariel Works, next door. George Morgan and two business associates purchased Midland Forging and set up George Morgan Ltd in 1933 and they continued to supply the needs of the local automotive industry until closure in 2000. (Archive Department, Birmingham Reference Library)

Tool making was just as important to Birmingham trade as press work. All presses were fitted with a 'tool', or 'tools', that shaped the metal when the press was closed. Each tool had to be made with precision and skill. Tool makers had to interpret engineering drawings and translate the dimensions to make the correct shape out of a piece of hard metal, frequently steel. A range of cutting, drilling and planing machines was utilised to produce the required form that often had to be accurate to a thousandth of an inch. Metal spinning was more than a skill, it was (and is) an art. Various metals, including aluminium and steel, were 'spun' on a lathe, working the metal against a wooden paddle that helped the spinner shape the piece into the form required.

The refining of precious metals and the cleaning of other metals such as steel encouraged the establishment of a local chemical industry. This industry diversified during the nineteenth century to include the production of fine chemicals for electroplating and colours for the paint trade. Once the making of town gas had been established a whole new range of chemical by-products became available for working up. Spent oxide from the gas works purifiers became a useful supply of sulphur for acid production.

Birmingham also became the centre of an important varnish industry. Varnishes were used to provide a protective coating for brassware and brought out the rich yellow colour of the different brasses, to enhance their ornamental qualities. All ingredients were imported from different parts of the globe and brought to Birmingham to be worked up as needed. Different formulations made to secret recipes formed the basis of the varnish trade. The local plastics industry developed out of the existing varnish industry, when synthetic resins came to be made in Birmingham.

Glass making was the result of mixing certain substances and heating in a furnace until molten. Sand and lead oxide were major ingredients in the process that made Flint Glass at the various glassworks in and around Birmingham. They produced fine examples of clear and coloured cut glass, while other firms concentrated on the supply of more mundane articles such as lenses for lamps or aspects for signals. Birmingham's glassmakers were most prevalent during the nineteenth century, although some carried on the trade well into the twentieth century. Numbered among the glassmakers in Birmingham was the work sometimes referred to as a 'Crib', where a master worked with one or two small pots. These were small operations, which employed only a few men and boys and made common glassware, such as cruets. There appear to have been five or six similar works distributed across Birmingham who made this basic glassware.

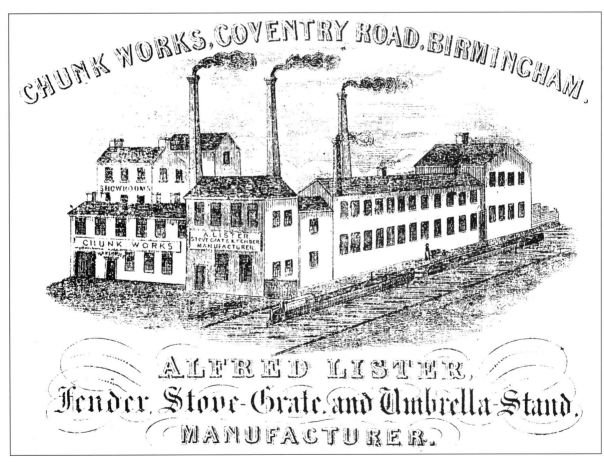

Chunk Works, Coventry Road. The naming of these premises is attributed to the original owner, Thomas Morton Jones, whose association with inventor Dr William Church led to the building of the Chunk Engine Works. Originally devoted to making engine parts and boring cylinders, it is possible that the railway locomotive engine designed by Dr Church was assembled here. Church's engine is remembered for the fatal boiler explosion at Bromsgrove in 1840, when two railway workers were killed. The Chunk Engine Works passed from Jones to Richard Prosser, who was a Birmingham-born engineer, and then to Alfred Lister. In Lister's time the premises were adapted to making fenders, stove grates and other castings. *(Cornish 1853 Guide)*

Birmingham engineering
firms manufactured a
diverse range of products.
Heenan & Froude
produced the Capel Fan
at a factory in Aston
before their move to
Worcester. This fan
was of particular use
for underground
ventilation in mines.
(Kelly's Directory)

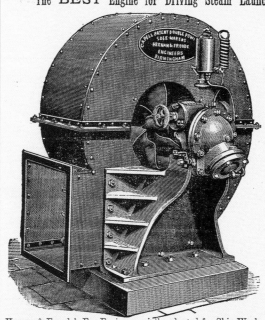

The "TOWER" Spherical Engine.

The BEST Engine for Driving Steam Launches, Dynamos, Fans, Pumps, &c.

High Speed with Economy and Compactness.

AWARDED

GOLD MEDAL

Inventions Exhibition.

THE CAPELL PATENT

DOUBLE-POWER FAN,

The most Powerful & Efficient Fan in the World.

For all duties—Blowing, Exhausting, Drying, Ventilating, &c.

Special Fans for Ship Work and for Colliery Ventilation.

SOLE MANUFACTURERS:

HEENAN & FROUDE,

NEWTON HEATH IRONWORKS, MANCHESTER.

CAPELL FAN WORKS, ASTON LANE,

BIRMINGHAM.

Heenan & Froude's Fan Engine, specially adapted for Ship Work.

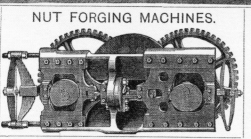
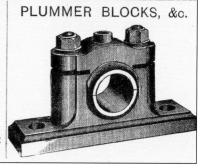

TAYLOR & CHALLEN,

ENGINEERS AND MACHINISTS,

Makers of Horizontal and other Steam Engines,

DERWENT FOUNDRY,

Constitution Hill, Birmingham.

PULLEYS.

NUT FORGING MACHINES.

NUT TAPPING, FACING, AND SHAPING MACHINES.

BOLT FORGING AND SCREWING MACHINES.

PLUMMER BLOCKS, &c.

ALSO MACHINERY FOR COINING, MAKING GUNPOWDER, GUN & RIFLE BARRELS, &c
BAND PULLEYS, COUPLINGS & SHAFTING, & GENERAL MACHINERY.

Taylor & Challen advert. The making of steam engines in the Birmingham district is commonly associated with the firm of Boulton & Watt at the Soho Manufactory and the Soho Foundry (Smethwick). Demand for stationary engines for civil undertakings, factories and local collieries encouraged other firms to construct and supply machinery, engines and related parts. Joseph Taylor embarked on his engine-making career first in leased premises in Brasshouse Yard, Broad Street, before moving across the road to take charge of Peter Capper's Broad Street Foundry. Another move took Taylor to Constitution Hill and a disused papier mâché factory, where the Derwent Foundry was established. *(Heartland Press Collection)*

The Austin car factory and munitions, Longbridge. Munition making during the First World War led to the building of several Midlands munitions factories. The Austin factory was considerably enlarged between 1915 and 1918 in order to deal with the amount of ammunition and ordnance vehicles produced there. *(Mike Oliver)*

Nineteenth-century industry presented many challenges for the makers of steam engines. Birmingham had its share of firms, which employed the skilled workforce that was required to produce precision-made parts so essential to the working of the engines. Birmingham cycle making was honed through the engineering skills developed in engine making, the gun trade and sewing machine manufacture. During the twentieth century, these skills were also adapted for the making of motorcycles, automobiles and aircraft components.

Another diverse use of engineering skills was the making of permanent and electro-magnets. The use of magnets as mineral and scrap separators or for lifting purposes developed during the twentieth century. Any list of the other diverse trades practised in Birmingham would be a lengthy one. The many aspects of the jewellery trade, gun making and the button trade are but some of those trades for which Birmingham is better known. Both metal- and wood-working skills were needed to make both upright and grand pianos, and local supplies of high quality steel wire assisted the establishment of piano making in the city. The skills of the wood worker were put to use in many other ways. Wood was fashioned and worked to make carriages

Billy Box set up the Electromagnets factory in Bond Street to make magnetic separation machines and electromagnets. *(Archives Department, Birmingham Reference Library)*

Shakespeare, Kirkland & Frost letterhead reproduced a photograph of the frontage of their cycle and motor works in Sampson Road North. Shakespeare & Co. were principally bicycle makers. (*Edwards Brothers MS*)

Below: Bicycle and tricycle making came to be an important trade in Birmingham, where engineering skills were taken to a new level. Quadrant Cycles of Sheepcote Street were among the pioneers in this trade. (*Heartland Press Collection*)

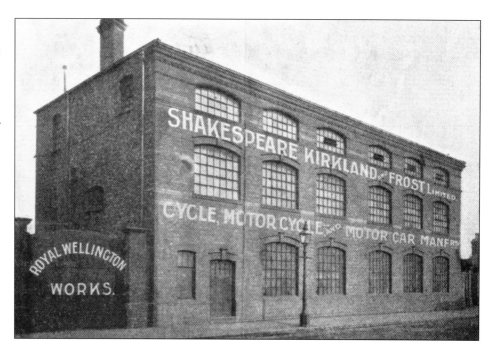

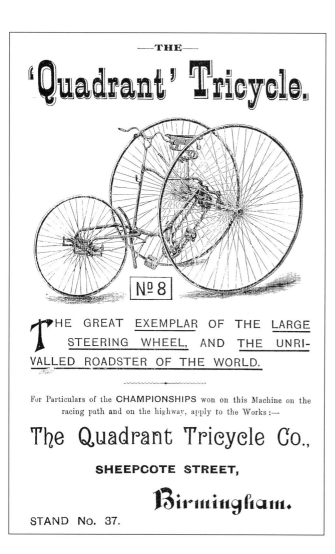

and carts and formed the bodywork for early automobiles. It was used in the making of bedsteads, canal boats, furniture, looking glasses and railway wagons.

Few people connect Birmingham with the leather trade, while many would associate leather working with nearby Walsall. Yet the town of Birmingham has hundreds of years of practice with the making of leather and leather goods. There were several tanneries in the Digbeth area that sent tanned hides to the Old Leather Hall, which was once located in New Street. Saddle making in Birmingham was still being carried on at the time of the Boer War and by 1910 some 80 firms still advertised as saddle and harness makers. These numbers gradually dwindled, but leather working has never left the city. Certain manufacturers came to specialise in the production of leather saddles for the cycle trade. Others produced leather upholstery for automobiles and carriages.

The sap of certain trees produced a type of latex known as Gutta-Percha, which found favour for certain uses in nineteenth-century Birmingham. Manufacturers would import this material to be worked up for footwear and related purposes. Another latex substance was rubber. The making of rubber goods flourished in twentieth-century Birmingham, when several tyre-making and rubber components

Working conditions in factories changed during the early years of the twentieth century. Mess, washing and toilet facilities were improved and at larger factories staff were encouraged to take part in social and sporting events. The concessions all helped to ease the monotony of the many repetitive tasks that were the daily lot of the worker. Here tea ladies are seen at the Birmingham Small Arms factory, Small Heath, making their rounds of the cycle and arms factory providing refreshment for the staff. *(Birmingham Museum & Art Galleries)*

firms were established in the town. These included international names like Dunlop, whose factories at Aston and later Erdington provided car tyres to customers across the globe.

Those employed in the food and drink industries adapted their skills in many ways. Birmingham had its share of breweries (for both beer and vinegar), bakeries, biscuit factories, chocolate makers, crisp makers, mineral water suppliers, tea blenders and toffee makers. Some famous and household names have originated in the city, including Bird's Custard Powder, Cadbury's Dairy Milk Chocolate and Typhoo Tea.

Modern Birmingham is now a multicultural city and today there are factories established for the production and distribution of foods to suit many needs. Most notable are the various Asian food factories that have grown up around the city in recent years.

Railway links were essential to the manufacturers of Birmingham. The three major companies, the Great Western, London & North Western and Midland Railway, all had depots in the city where goods packed in open wagons and closed vans were received and sent out by the trainload. Manufacturers had the choice of railway company and dealt with those who could best serve their needs. For Scotland and the North East the

Tame Valley Canal, Deykins Avenue. *(Black Country Living Musuem)*

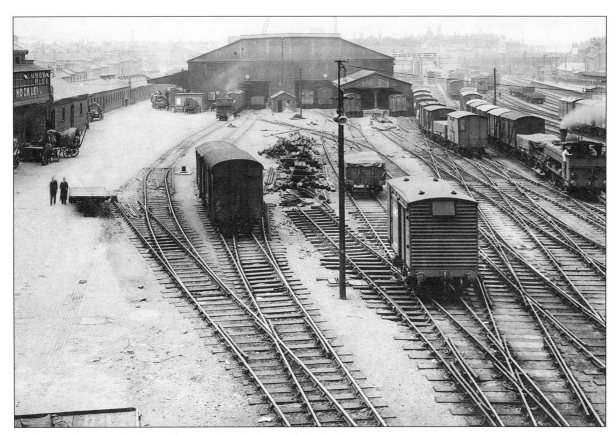

Hockley Goods station, looking north, 1939. *(Heartland Press Collection)*

LNWR or Midland might be preferred, while destinations in the South West and Wales would be placed with the Great Western. Hockley Goods was owned by the Great Western Railway and was their major depot for Birmingham. Horse-drawn and motor lorries and vans ferried goods and materials between Hockley and the business premises.

The canal network aided the development of the town of Birmingham, moving manufactured goods to destinations throughout Britain or abroad via the ports. Canal trade continued for nearly 200 years. In the illustration opposite a narrowboat is seen loading with parts destined for the Hardy Spicer Factory at Chester Road, Erdington. Other features in this view include the canal lock house, the GEC power station and the Birmingham Canal Navigations pumping station house.

Road cartage and carriage has changed over the years. An important trade across the city was the carter who carried for the different firms transporting manufactured goods and component parts. Many firms maintained a fleet of commercial vehicles for their trading needs. Until the 1920s carriage was principally horse-drawn throughout the town. Firms were put to the expense of buying horses and looking after their welfare. Stable blocks were provided and lucrative business for the carriage builder was maintained. In this photograph a pair of houses are linked up to a Davenports delivery wagon. Davenports were brewers in Bath Row, Birmingham, who set up a home delivery service for their beer and required an extensive fleet of delivery vehicles. *(Davenports MSS, Birmingham Library Archives)*

CHAPTER 1

SEWING MACHINE MANUFACTURE

The invention of the mechanical sewing machine was a great asset to the clothing manufacturer. Production of garments was made possible on a far greater scale than was achieved through hand stitching. The basic concepts of the sewing machine, which included the shuttle mechanism and lock-stitch, were developed during the nineteenth century by American inventors, and it was in America that the manufacture of industrial sewing machines progressed. Elias Howe devised the lock-stitch method and took out a patent in the USA during 1846. Finding little interest in America, Howe sent his brother to Britain and found interest with William Thomas, a corset and bag maker from Cheapside, London. Thomas arranged for Elias Howe to come to London and work for him to produce a machine suitable for stitching corsets. Howe, on his return to America, found that several manufacturers had taken up sewing machine making and instituted a legal battle to recover his patent rights.

Early machines had an intermittent feed, but in 1849 Allen Benjamin Wilson improved the design with an automatic system. Two prominent American manufacturers that came to supply the British market were Wheeler & Wilson and the Singer Manufacturing Co. Both firms sent parts to Britain for assembly and sale. Wheeler & Wilson's product was initially popular with some clothing manufacturers, building up stocks of hundreds of units. Gradually Singer, which was the first to cater for the family as well as the manufacturer, overtook Wheeler & Wilson's sales.

British inventors were not idle during this period, and eventually new variations on the design were patented in Britain. William Frederick Thomas (the son of William Thomas) produced a range of sewing patents from 1853. An early maker of British sewing machines was the Bradbury factory in Oldham, Lancashire, but such was the number of foundries and press-working firms in the West Midlands that sewing machine manufacture was concentrated in Birmingham and Coventry.

Local trade directories published during the 1870s have a lengthy list of sewing machine makers, although a fair proportion were agents and suppliers for machines produced elsewhere. Thomas sewing machines were manufactured in Birmingham by Charles & William Harwood, who were die and press-tool makers at 54 New Summer Street. As trade increased premises were acquired in New Loveday Street, which became known as the Britannia Foundry.

Nottingham-born Arthur Maxfield was the owner of several sewing machine patents that led to the design and production of the Agenoria model. Together with Isaac Cole and Charles Fowke, Maxfield formed the Franklin Sewing Machine Co. in 1868. The Franklin Sewing Machine Works was set up on the corner of Musgrave Road and Park Road, Hockley and remained in their ownership until 1874. Isaac Cole left the firm to set up in business in Edinburgh. In January 1873 Cole signed an agreement with Maxfield for the supply of Agenoria sewing machines, whereby Maxfield would supply at least 18 machines each week to Cole. Isaac Cole was also given the rights to sell

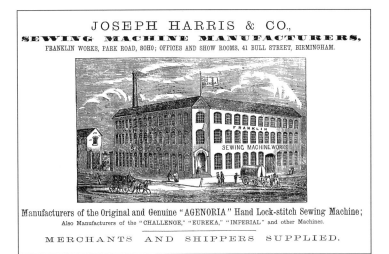

The Franklin Sewing Machine Works, Park Road.

Agenoria machines in Scotland and elsewhere in the world, while Arthur Maxfield retained the rights to sell in England, Wales and the Channel Islands.

The resulting changes at the Franklin Works were accompanied by the takeover by Joseph Harris and John Judson. Joseph Harris had a variety of business interests and owned a steam-powered dyeing works in Birmingham. He also became an agent for the sale of different brands of sewing machines. Harris & Judson produced the Challenge and also supplied Agenoria sewing machines. They also changed the name of the factory to the Imperial Works. Arthur Maxfield moved to 71 and 72 Spencer Street, where the Agenoria machine continued to be made. Rights to make both the Agenoria and Challenge models were sold to the Royal Sewing Machine Co. in 1877, when the Imperial Works were closed.

Another event of 1877 was the closing of the Breech Action Manufacturing Works at Small Heath. Known as the Regents Works, this factory had been established in 1871 and adjoined the Royal Sewing Machine Factory. It engaged in the varied trade of making Martini-Henry breech actions, sewing machines and roller skates.

Sewing machine making was a competitive trade, and works closures and bankruptcies were regular events within the industry. Names that came and went included the firms Thomas Barton (Lionel Street), The Birmingham Manufacturing Co. (36 Holloway Head), Greville, Harston & Co. and Thomas Slater (18 and 19 Edmund Street). Charles and William Harwood faced similar problems. They transferred their business to 101 Newtown Row, where Thomas machines continued to be made. Their new premises comprised upper and lower workshops complete with foundry and a smith's shop. Harwoods formed the Harwoods London Machine Co. Ltd, which was quickly in financial trouble and suffered liquidation in 1875. The factory was then taken over by W.F. Thomas & Co., who continued sewing machine making there until about 1884. William Harwood carried on a separate business making and repairing sewing machines in a part of the Old Mill, Porchester Street, Aston, until April 1877.

Newton Wilson & Co. and the Royal Machine Manufacturing Co. Ltd were numbered among the more successful and longer-lived companies. The Royal Machine Manufacturing Co. (of Herberts Road, Small Heath) was formed in 1868 and was associated with Thomas Shakespear & Co., who sold their products through their depot at 32 Union Street. Shakespear had been agents in Birmingham for Wheeler & Wilson's models since 1860, but lost the agency about the time the Royal was established. Shakespear then started to advertise Wheeler & Wilson machines made at the Herbert Road Works. It was a situation which the Wheeler & Wilson Manufacturing Co. of Broadway, New York, contested. In 1869 Wheeler & Wilson published advertisements in the Birmingham papers that Shakespear had no authority to sell their sewing machines, represent them or use their name. Wheeler & Wilson models were sold through an office in the Exchange Buildings, Stephenson Place in Birmingham. Shakespear, at the time, advertised Wheeler and Wilson models alongside the Shakespeare Lock-Stitch hand machine. They continued to run their advertisements for a time using the term 'Royal' Wheeler & Wilson but eventually withdrew all mention of the Wheeler & Wilson name and simply called this model of machines the Royal.

The Royal Sewing Machine factory comprised a range of two- and three-storey shops that included show rooms, packing rooms, machine shops, fitting shops, screw making shops, wheel shop, rim shop, smithies and stoves. They produced a range of different brands that had been devised by themselves or acquired from other manufacturers: the Shakespear, Windsor, Times, Challenge and Agenoria were numbered among their product lines in 1878.

The firm of Newton Wilson and Co. owed its origin principally to William Newton Wilson, whose patents of the early 1860s included several improvements to the basic sewing machine design. Wilson, who traded from 144 High Holborn in London, had previously patented a washing machine in 1858. In 1860 William Wilson described himself as manufacturer of sewing machines when some improvements were suggested in his next patent petition that incorporated information supplied by Lucius Bijeleur of Boston, USA. Wilson set up a factory in Birmingham, first in Floodgate Street and subsequently at 52 Pope Street, in the Jewellery Quarter. The St George's Foundry was established at the Pope Street works and it was here that Princess of Wales brand of machine was produced.

One of the trademarks of the Royal Sewing Machine Co.

Mechanical sewing machines had a ready market among garment makers and the leather trade. One local tailor contributed to the pool of invention through devising an improved machine for making buttonholes. James Moore Clements had a tailor's shop in Livery Street when, in 1862, he was granted a patent for a new arrangement of stitching the hole. The success of the design enabled him to set up his own works.

Some firms chose to specialise in the making of components, rather than make complete machines. William Bown (of 308 Summer Lane) was one who founded a business for the supply of sewing machine components such as shuttles, shuttle reels, springs, binders, hemmers and tuckers. Bown's business had been established in 1860, and he prospered by selling sewing machine parts and components for bicycles and tricycles. A notable achievement on its part was the purchase of the licence for hill-climbing gearing for velocipedes, which was to prove to be an important benefit for cyclists. Bown's involvement with sewing machines continued to diversify as new ideas and concepts evolved. During 1885 and 1886 the firm became associated with the Moldacot Pocket Sewing Machine Co. of London for the supply of 50,000 pocket sewing machines.

The demand for bicycles created a new industry for the Midlands and led to the sewing machine makers adapting their business to cycle manufacture. The Royal Machine Manufacturing Co., of Small Heath, added the making of bicycles and tricycles to their range and gradually ran down their sewing machine trade, while William Bown also concentrated on the making of cycle components. Newton Wilson & Co. changed their name to the St George's Engineering Co. They made the New Rapid bicycles and tricycles and came to concentrate on this aspect of the trade during the 1880s. Sewing machine making ceased at Pope Street in 1887, when the foundry plant, with cupola, crane, sand mill, moulding boxes, ladles, patterns and pig and scrap iron used for making sewing machines, was offered for sale.

A few firms still traded as manufacturers, such as the Two Reel Sewing Machine Co. Ltd (Albion Street) and the Ernest Street Sewing Machine Works (Holloway Head), but only one, Smith, North & Priestman (Ellis Street), remained in the trade after 1900. Agents continued to deal in the sale of machines assembled elsewhere, but the large-scale production of sewing machines was now left to factories in other locations. Most notable perhaps was the Singer factory at Kilbowie on the River Clyde, near Glasgow.

CHAPTER TWO

WIRE & NAILS

The method of wire drawing was briefly discussed in *Birmingham's Industrial Heritage* (Sutton Publishing, 2002). Wire made from ferrous and non-ferrous metals was worked up to a variety of products that included crinolines, fish-hooks, nails, needles, pins, screws, springs and umbrella frames. Steel and iron wire was employed in the making cables, hawsers and ropes, while special quality steel wire proved suitable for piano wire. Wire was fashioned to make chains for lamps, chandeliers or scales. It also was an essential component for fenders, fire guards, meat safes, rat traps and window blinds.

Thick wires were generally used for fencing and telegraph purposes, while finer wires were required for hooks and eyes, needles and pins. The firm of Sharp & Brown, Fazeley Street, established in 1853, adopted a process that changed little with the years. Their mill was capable of producing nearly 100 tons of wire per week. Iron was delivered by canal boat from the Stourbridge iron manufacturers in bars 20ft long by 2in square. These were then cut into shorter lengths, of about 3ft long, and heated in a furnace until red hot. Each bar was drawn into a rod, some fifty times its original length. The rod was then cooled and coiled up on a wheel. The coils were then pickled in acid, and left for the attentions of the wire drawer, who reduced the diameter of the rods to wire of the required thickness.

WIRE DRAWERS

Not every manufacturer had the equipment or skills to draw the wire down to the necessary widths, and demand for specific diameters of metal wire sustained a number of firms which acted as middlemen working up wire to suit the needs of specific customers. Frederick A. Power supplied bright drawn steel wires of different thicknesses to a number of customers. This firm was established in about 1877 on vacant land beside Metropolitan Road, Saltley, that became known as the Midland Mills. It later moved to the Adderley Park Mills, which had been vacated by the Birmingham Metals & Munitions Co. during 1919. These works were subsequently enlarged when Power's came to occupy the adjacent Union Paper Mills when Smith, Stone & Knight concentrated their business at Catells Grove.

Wire drawing was a particular skill, as wire had to be drawn with accuracy, often to a thousandth of an inch. Drawing was also a team effort where a drawer and loader worked together for each machine. The loader put the wire onto the machine, while the drawer set the process in motion and was responsible for the successive die settings that reduced the wire to the required diameter.

Power owned several different types of drawing machines. One type was known as the 'Longholer', where a coil of steel wire was drawn through a die box onto a 'Diablo' shaped drum. This drum then fed through another die box to a second drum and so the process was repeated with dies and take-up drums until the required thickness was achieved. Every pass through the die reduced the diameter of the wire by degree, and banks of five or eight 'Diablos' and die boxes were arranged in each Longholer. With every pass through the die, the wire was lubricated by soapy water. Each batch of wire was pointed before being set through the die, and subsequent lengths of wire were soldered onto the preceding one, so that a continuous process was set up. This was a physically demanding job, with workers constantly handling heavy coils of steel, but once a pattern had been established skilled loaders and drawers could process up to 24 tons of wire a day.

Firms like Power produced rolls of wire to a range of thicknesses and these were sold for a variety of uses. Some were exported, others found use in the local mattress, nail and screw factories.

WIRE WEAVING

The firm of G. Baker & Co., Birmingham Wiremills & Wireworks, Chester Street, received wire from the wire makers in rough coils. Iron, copper and brass wire were purchased in different lengths and delivered to the Chester Street Works for weaving into mesh and netting or making into chandelier chains. Wire was 'pickled' in long troughs containing a special mixture of acid and lime before being reduced to required thickness through drawing.

Baker's business as described in 1880 reveals a factory capable of working wire into many forms. Baker's own patent chain-making machines were devised in about 1848. These machines were capable of taking brass wire and forming it into lengths of double-link brass chain, each link having its circles neatly bent, ends turned in and hanging around the next link. In another part of the factory upholsterers' nails and staples were turned out.

Wire netting was made by the aid of bobbins and a frame, but during the 1850s a new development copied the process used in the Nottingham lace-netting machine and Baker & Sons purchased a machine based on these principles for their Aston factory. The partnership that comprised the firm of George Baker & Co. was dissolved during November 1883 and the plant at the Birmingham Wiremills & Wireworks, Chester Street was offered by sale by auction on Monday 17 December 1883. Baker then transferred his business to premises in 68 Cecil Street, where the business of wire working and weaving was continued through to the twentieth century. George Baker died in 1895, but members of the Baker family continued to run Cecil Street Works.

Other adaptations of the wire weaving trade included mattress manufacture, which became a staple trade in Birmingham alongside the metallic bedstead trade and wire grid work for paper manufacture.

HOOK AND EYE MANUFACTURE

Laces, pins and buckles were commonly used to hold garments in place. Another more specialist type of fastening was the hook and eye arrangement. Thin wire was fashioned into hooks and eyes for the clothing industry, where they were used on certain types of undergarments. Birmingham became an important centre for the trade, which developed during the early years of the nineteenth century. Over twenty different firms included hook and eyes as part of their trade, but one, owned by the Newey family, deserves the lion's share of the credit for the establishment of the hook and eye in Birmingham.

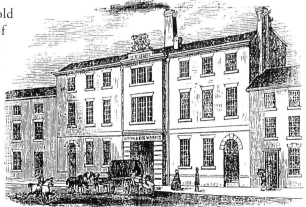

Newey Factory, 54 Brearley Street. Hooks and eyes were produced at the original three-storey factory near the corner of Summer Lane and Brearley Street. *(Kelly's Trade Directory)*

A 1960s advertisement showing the range of fasteners supplied by Newey's. *(Birmingham Chamber of Commerce Journal)*

The frontages of buildings in Brearley Street still comprise a mixture of industrial properties, May 2000. *(Ray Shill)*

Newey's former factory in Brearley Street, May 2000. The Newey family owned a group of adjoining buildings in Brearley Street and Summer Lane. In addition to the original factory there were shops and houses, which were eventually incorporated into the factory site. The original factory building still has the stone plaque advertising its royal patronage. *(Ray Shill)*

Richard Newey began the family business making steel toys in Birmingham during the latter half of the eighteenth century. These included shoe-buckles, whip mounts and watch keys which were made by stamping and pressing at a factory in Loveday Street. Richard Newey died in 1798 and the business passed to his son James. In 1804 the business was moved to Summer Lane, where hook and eye fasteners were first made. James George Newey joined the firm in 1820 and later succeeded his father in the business. He patented a new design of hook and eye, called the Swan Bill Hook, in 1846. It proved to be a practical design and generated many sales for Newey. A new factory was constructed in Brearley Street in 1850, which still stands. Some of the toy range, which included split rings for ale and gas taps, also continued to be made at Brearley Street.

During the First World War Newey's made fastenings for many clothing items, ranging for greycoats to gun belts. Newey's continued to specialise in the fastener trade after the war, and retained a separate existence until merging with pin makers D.F. Tayler in 1934.

PIN MAKING

Pins were commonly made from brass wire cut to length, headed, and dipped in tin. Several pin-making firms were established in Birmingham. They sold their produce to the wholesale drapers and to haberdashers or for export through Birmingham-based export merchants.

The making of a simple pin required several processes. It was once a very labour-intensive trade, but was mechanised in the Victorian era through the development of machines that made pins directly from wire. Thorpe, Latham & Kilminster had a pin works in Lancaster Street, which originally made pins by the old method. A description of pin making at their works was published in West's Warwickshire Directory that was published in 1830. Some twelve separate processes were evidently needed to make a pin.

Thorpe, Latham & Kilminster's factory at 5 Lancaster Street was taken over by the firm of Palmer & Holt. During 1840 an inspection was made by R.D. Grainger to examine the conditions in which children were employed at the two Birmingham pin factories belonging to Palmer & Holt and to Thomas Phipson & Son, which provides graphic details of the way children were treated. Boys and girls as young as seven years were employed in the heading shops from 8 a.m till 7 or 8 p.m.

Thomas Phipson & Son had a long history of pin making in Birmingham and could trace their firm back to start of the trade in the town. Samuel Ryland had commenced wire drawing and pin making there during the middle of the eighteenth century. Ryland established a pin factory in New Street, which passed into the ownership of his nephew, Thomas Phipson Jnr. Thomas Phipson & Son remained at New Street until the mid-1830s, when they transferred to a canal-side factory at 12 Broad Street. They occupied these premises for some ten years before moving again to Mott Street.

A description of the pin manufactory of Messr Thorpe, Latham, and Kilminster near to the Birmingham and Fazeley Canal (*West's Directory* 1830, p. 223)

We were highly gratified in viewing with what celerity the twelve different processes were gone through, in forming and completing an article, of which four times that number of the manufactured article are disposed of for one half penny. The 1st process, is that of cleaning the wire when received from the mill.

2nd The wire drawer

3rd The straightener

4th The pointer, who cuts the wire into six lengths, in 400 or 500 in one handful, although the shears will only admit of the wire being laid flat, and every pin cut distinctly.

5th The pointer holds and points about forty at a time, in almost an instant.

6th The header

7th The head drawer; this part of the process requires peculiarly fine tools.

8th The twister of the wire, which form the heads

9th The head cutter, who cuts about fourteen at one stroke

10th The whitener, under whom the pin goes through several processes

11th The sticker on the papers, in which a small scored frame is used, as a guide to fix a row instantaneously

12th The making them up in packets for the market

Perhaps there are not so many curious operations in the manufactory of any article at so low a price, or where the trade requires more nicety, or greater capital, in proportion to the article manufactured. The establishment of Messrs Thorpe and Co., is of recent date, but rapidly on the increase, they employ upwards of 300 persons, within and outside the walls of their manufactory, to which the greatest attention is paid by its liberal and spirited proprietors.

Mechanisation for certain pin-making processes reduced the amount of manual work and considerably increased production. The degree of mechanisation varied from firm to firm. There were machines capable of taking coils of wire, which cut out individual pin lengths, then pointed and headed each pin, leaving the pins to be whitened and packed. Other pin makers chose to have separate machines for pointing and heading.

Whitening was performed in copper vessels heated on a fire. The pins were boiled in water for about one hour, along with grains of tin and an amount of potassium bi-tartrate. They were then removed, thoroughly washed, dried and then polished in bran. The pins were finally separated from the bran by a machine that sifted the bran, winnow fashion, clear of the pins.

Birmingham pin makers were slow to adopt mechanical processes. Cornish's guide for 1853 mentioned that the principal makers took coils of pin wire to be first straightened and then cut into pieces of six or eight pins in length, which were afterwards reduced to the length of a single pin. Each pin was headed through the application of pressure, pointed on a small grindstone turned by steam, silvered by being dipped in a solution of tin and then packed.

Hand pointing was continued as a specialist trade by a select group of skilled workers. They took rolls of wire and straightened it on a board before cutting to lengths of about 30ft each. These lengths were then cut down again to smaller lengths before being delivered to the pointers. Hand pointing was performed on two revolving steel-file wheels: one had a coarse texture, the other was fine textured. The first wheel roughened the tip down and the second finished it. Thirty or forty pin wires were applied to the wheels at one time and by the dextrous action of the workman both ends of the wire were pointed. The wire was then cut into two pieces and the un-pointed ends were headed by machine.

All the above processes were adopted to produce the common solid-headed pin. There was another method that involved the spinning of wire and the cutting of 'heads'. These heads were then punched onto the pointed wire using hand dies. This method of pin making was entirely superseded by the making of solid-head pins.

Peyton & Isles, of Peel Works, Macdonald Street, were extensively engaged in the production of solid-head pins, hooks and eyes, corset and drapery hooks, metal brace and pearl shirt buttons, studs and hairpins. They were among the first pin makers, if not the first, to attach the pins to cardboard shapes illustrated with artistic views. This firm began as a partnership between Richard Peyton and Charles Isles at 96 High Street, Bordesley, where Peyton had a separate partnership in making beds with Jonathan Harlow (see Chapter 4). The Peel Works were established in about 1851 and eventually passed into the sole ownership of Charles Isles.

An important pin-making industry was carried out in Gloucestershire, where water-powered mills worked brass from the Bristol area into pins. By 1802 pin making in the town of Gloucester alone employed one fifth of the population. It was in Gloucester that William Cowcher made his fortune by pin making from brass wire, and it was this business founded by the Cowcher family, in 1743, that later took Robert Kirby, George Beard and William Tovey into partnership. Eventually their business became known as Kirby, Beard & Co.

Kirby, Beard & Co. introduced mechanisation into their factory when Seth Hunt's pin making machine was installed during 1818. It was an invention that used soft wire, and pins made by this process had the disadvantage of being easily bent. The machinery was also difficult to handle. An American, Lemanuel W. Wright, later came to work for Kirby, Beard and attempted to improve Hunt's machinery. Wright then left Kirby, Beard to develop an improved version. Wright's pin-making machine also had its faults, but the design had sufficient merit for competitor D.F. Tayler to take up the design. Wright's patent, taken out in 1824, was considered a crucial development for the pin makers. His machine was capable of making entire pins from a roll of wire.

Daniel Foote Taylor and Henry Shuttleworth made pins at Lightpill Mill, near Stroud, from 1825. Shuttleworth carried on the pin trade when Tayler died in 1840, but, lacking Tayler's business skill, led the firm on the downward trail to bankruptcy in 1843. The business and pin-making patents were sold to Peter Edelsten and John

Below: The Newhall Works, April 2000. The impressive frontage to the Newhall Works, which faces George Street, has changed little over the years despite major alterations to the rear of the building. *(Ray Shill)*

Williams, who moved their equipment to Birmingham, in about 1847. The next year the Newhall Works, in George Street, was acquired. William Benyon, stamper and piecer, had formerly used these premises to make a variety of items that ranged from buttons to hooks and eyelets. Now Edelsten and Williams converted the Newhall Works to make pins under their name and the name of D.F. Tayler & Co. The site was gradually enlarged to include rolling mills, and a copper and brass wire mill. The wire mills were started as a separate business, in about 1852, under the name of Edelsten, Williams & Edelsten. A printing and packing section was opened in a new building in Newhall Hill during 1866, where pin cards were printed.

A description of the Newhall Works in 1871 mentioned an organisation dedicated to wire drawing, pin and hairpin making. Wire was received in large coils of wide gauge and drawn through rolls to reduce the diameter. The treatment left the metal brittle, and to rectify this problem the drawn wire was annealed by placing it in large cast-iron, cylindrical-shaped pots and heating it in annealing furnaces. It was then taken from the pots, and again went through a process of rolling till it was reduced in some instances to almost the fineness of thread. Not all wire was used for pins: many tons of wire were prepared for securing the corks in bottles containing effervescing drinks.

The wire required for pin making was transferred to the machine room, where the coils were placed on drums. The pin was completed in one machine, which straightened the wire, cut it to length, formed the heads and pointed the pins. These were then collected and were finally boiled in tin to prepare them for use. From this one establishment upwards of 60 million pins were sent out every week. Hairpins were also made with the same facility and rapidity. The wire-drawing and pin-making companies remained individual entities until 1886, when they were combined in the firm of D.F. Tayler Ltd.

Birmingham, in the 1840s and 1850s, had become a beacon that attracted new business, and pin makers Edelsten & Williams were not the only pin-making firm to relocate there. George Goodman moved to Caroline Street. He first began making needles in Wootten Wawen in 1810 and had moved to another water mill at Henley-in-Arden, where he traded as Lane & Goodman, before settling in Birmingham during 1842. Goodman became specially known for the manufacture of safety pins. Goodman purchased patent rights from Samuel Bagnall during 1892, which helped his firm establish a reputation for the making of safety pins. Goodman's business was transferred to new premises located in Robin Hood Lane, Hall Green, during 1910. It was purchased by GKN in 1938.

In 1853 Kirby, Beard also moved to Birmingham, where they made pins at the Lion Works, in Richard Street. As trade improved larger premises at the Ravenhurst Works in Bradford Street were taken. German bombing gutted Kirby, Beard's factory in December 1940 and manufacture was moved to temporary premises at 498–506 Moseley Street. The firm rebuilt the Ravenhurst Works after the war and continued the production of hairgrips, pins and needles there until 1958.

D.F. Tayler increased their share of the haberdashery market through the takeover of several other related businesses after 1919. They bought needle makers W.R. Steel, of Redditch, in 1920 and during 1925 Lemet Metal Works were also purchased. Lemet made spokes and nipples for pram and bike wheels. Hook and eye makers Newey and D.F. Tayler merged in 1934 and the corporate name Newey & Tayler was adopted for the group, although the works retained an independent existence. The new group was split into four divisions. One produced non-ferrous wire and strip, a second made steel wire. The third included pin making and hook and eyes. The fourth dealt with the printing and packaging needs for the whole group. The printing and packaging department was moved to a new site at Tipton during 1936. The next year a new plating factory was opened, alongside the existing plant at Tipton.

During the war much of Newey's production was taken up with the making of munitions. Cartridges for anti-aircraft guns were made at Tipton from brass rolled at Tayler's mills in George Street. Postwar, Newey & Tayler continued to operate from various sites. Newey Brothers had premises in Brearley Street (head office) and Tipton that embraced all fasteners, needles, pins and hairpins. Metal and wire working was conducted at Newhall Street and Carver Street, while the Lemet Metal Works still concentrated on the manufacture of spokes, nipples and washers.

Goodman introduced a major innovation. The snap-lock safety pin for fastening babies' nappies, made from stainless steel wire, soon proved a popular product with mothers across the world. A close relationship was also established between Goodman and Newey Brothers. George Goodman sat on the board of Newey and there was an interchange of products. Newey supplied Goodman with straight pins and Goodman reciprocated with safety pins. Goodman had built up an important reputation in the industry. He persuaded the GKN board to invest in machinery for mass production of hairgrips with a plastic tip. Kirby, Beard also made hairgrips and was internationally known for the brand name Kirbigrip. The new Goodman product was enough to influence Kirby, Beard to sell their business to Goodman. Negotiations were opened and a favourable offer was received from GKN for the purchase of Kirby, Beard shares in 1957. Kirby, Beard was sold to GKN, and during 1958 it was decided to close the Ravenhurst Works and move production to the Goodman factory, in Hall Green.

In 1963 GKN decided to sell Goodman to Newey & Tayler. The head office was moved from Brearley Street to Hall Green following the takeover. Production and profits increased; by 1966 turnover had hit the £7.2 million mark. During the 1970s the range of Newey products continued to diversify and came to include the factoring of car windscreen covers, slimming preparations and anti-smoking aids.

Factories and offices owned by the group were distributed throughout Britain and the world, and the organisation had become somewhat diffuse. Newey & Tayler sold their Metal and Wire Division in order to finance the new product range. Both D.F. Tayler and Lemet Metal Works ceased to be a member of the Newey Group from 1973, when they were transferred to become part of the Delta Metal empire.

The decision to diversify may have been ill-advised. The roller-coaster of success ground to a halt during the mid-1970s and Newey's trading suffered, like that of so many other Birmingham-based firms. The German-based William Prym-Werke was allowed to buy a 25 per cent stake in Newey's in 1978 to assist with the finances. Within the year they had purchased the whole of Newey Group.

Bryan Knight became chief executive and commenced a programme of reform. One concern was that the manufacturing plant operated from three sites: at Brearley Street, Hall Green and Tipton. There was a large workforce and no single product was started or finished in the same place. Another problem was that haircare product sales were in decline, mainly through changes of style and fashion. Newey's haircare trade was sold to competitors Laughton & Son of Warstock. The sale enabled Newey to rationalise their business, close the Brearley Street and Hall Green factories and concentrate production at Tipton.

Laughton's could trace their roots to the firm of Jarrett & Rainsford, who began as pin makers in Birmingham. Stephen Jarrett was another Gloucestershire pin maker, who in 1860 moved to Birmingham, where he set up in business with Charles Rainsford at the pin factory formerly occupied by Palmer & Blackham at 7 Broad Street, Islington. Pins and some gilt jewellery were made there. Some ten years later the address of their factory was renumbered to 48 when Islington and Easy Row were combined. Charles Rainsford also purchased Jarrett's interest in the firm during the 1870s.

Jarrett & Rainsford became a limited company in 1908, and in 1909 relocated to the larger factory premises when they purchased the disused cabinet factory in Kent Street, known as the Alexandra Works.

G.A. Laughton was elected director for Jarrett & Rainsford in 1912. Laughton had been a manager employed by the firm, who set up Stratton & Co., a firm of stampers and piercers that made gilt and imitation jewellery. Stratton was the name of a fictional hero, whom Mrs Laughton had recently read about. Stratton's retained a separate existence to Jarrett & Rainsford, trading first from 148 Conybere Street, then the Balmoral Works, 58 Bromsgrove Street.

Origins of Stratton & Co. *(From A Century of Achievement, the Laughton Story 1860–1960)*

In the year of the Coronation of King George V, 1911, G.A. Laughton was running a small section of Jarrett & Rainsfords, selling coronation badges, flags, and so on. Certain component parts were made by a man named Carter who had a small work-shop. Owing to drink, his business was running down and he was delivering badly. He came on Saturday morning stating he had no money to pay his workers, consisting of two girls, and that he would have to close his business down, but he would sell his four hand-presses for £50 and then work at 50s per week. G.A. Laughton visited his works – it was a small work-shop approached by a rickety staircase. The plant consisted of four hand-presses, a few tools, some benching; and he had two girls working on the presses, plus his own labour. Being desperately in need of goods G.A.L. closed the bargain and agreed to employ him provided he would keep sober, which he did for two weeks only.

Stratton's became a considerable user of Duralumin, an aluminium alloy, during the First World War, when engaged in munitions work. Herbert Clark, manager to the Duralumin supplier, James Booth of Sheepcote Street, suggested a peacetime use once hostilities had ceased and Laughton chose to use this alloy for making knitting pins. Meanwhile Jarrett & Rainsford enlarged their factory when, in about 1919, a section of the Stanley Works in Kent Street was purchased. Here the firm used the additional space to make cardboard boxes, cork mats and model boats.

G.A. Laughton gained complete control of both companies during 1920. Jarrett & Rainsford and Stratton's merged to create Jarrett, Rainsford & Laughton Ltd, but still traded under their respective names. The company activities also continued to diversify. Strattons entered the radio market during 1923, making complete radio sets at their Balmoral Works. Jarrett & Rainsford carried on the hairpin and haircare trade. Women's hairstyles changed after the First World War; the fashion for long hair was replaced by one favouring short hair. Hairpin demand was reduced and plant capable of making 6 tons of hairpins per week became virtually redundant. The firm concentrated their efforts on new ranges of 'smallware' that became the 'Lady Jayne' brand of wave clips, hair curlers and hairgrips. New ranges in men's jewellery included cuff links that were developed during 1928, thanks to the efforts of Ernest Peet, a foreman tool maker working for Stratton's, who invented a version of expanding cuff link.

Production of the new and varied ranges led to further building expansion. The Leominster works was a new factory built in Lower Essex Street. Here in 1937 a hairgrip and hairpin manufacturing plant was installed alongside machinery for hair curler, curl clip and wave clip production. Other new ranges included lipstick containers made from non-ferrous metal, powder boxes and fancy vanity boxes (compacts). Many of these new products came to be made in plastic (see Chapter 7).

Jarrett, Rainsford & Laughton's factories in the centre of Birmingham were seriously damaged during 1940. Production was moved to the Lido at Warstock. These premises were extensively enlarged after the war to include the main offices, and production lines for the haircare products.

SCREW & NAIL MANUFACTURE

Kings Norton Screw factory. The engraving shows an early view of the Patent Screw Works, Kings Norton. *(GKN Magazine)*

Whenever the building trade was considered, the humble nail proved to be of great assistance to the carpenter. Early nails were hand made from metals such as iron. The making of hand-made nails became a family trade, where the husband, wife and children all played their part. With increased mechanisation in industry, machines were developed that could cut nail shapes from metal sheets and the 'cut-nail' industry was developed.

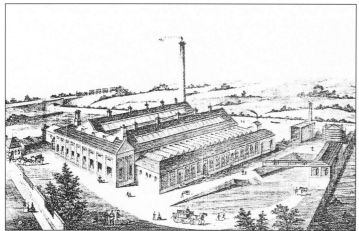

Another development was the manufacture of screws, which gave further aid to the carpenter in fixing wood to wood or other articles. The making of wood screws in twentieth-century Britain was frequently associated with the name of Guest, Keen & Nettlefold, a company that was formed in 1902. GKN had interests in many aspects of the iron trade. The making of screws was the responsibility of the GKN Screw Division.

James & Son made screws at a factory in Bradford Street, but needed space to

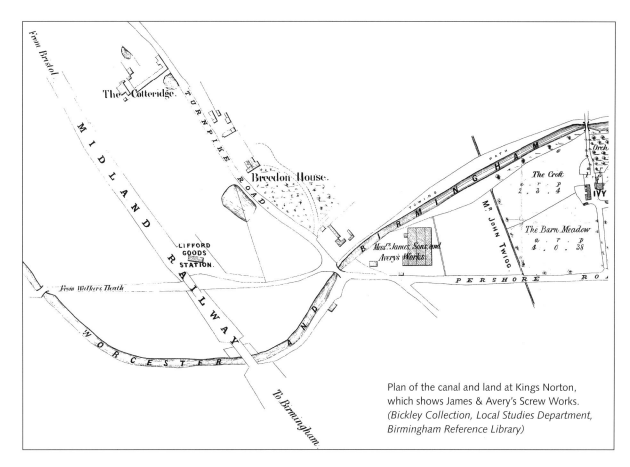

Plan of the canal and land at Kings Norton,
which shows James & Avery's Screw Works.
(Bickley Collection, Local Studies Department,
Birmingham Reference Library)

Chamberlain & Nettlefold
factory, Broad Street,
Birmingham. Nettlefold's
first Birmingham factory
was located on the corner
of Broad Street and
Baskerville Place. The
buildings were part of the
estate developed by
Thomas Gibson, which
included mills, wharves
and canal basins.
Chamberlain &
Nettlefold's premises
occupied an end strip of
land that ran the length
of Baskerville Place.
(GKN Magazine)

expand the business. In 1861 they purchased 3 acres of land at Kings Norton which
bordered the Worcester & Birmingham Canal. Funds for the buildings and plant were
raised by a mortgage agreement made in February 1862 that secured £5,000 towards the
cost. Work then went ahead with the first buildings that comprised two mill bays, an
engine house, boiler house, fitting shop, foundry and blacksmith's shop. There was lodge
at the gates and a gas plant to light the works. In 1864 Mr W. Avery joined the

partnership, which then became James & Avery. W. Avery had previously been manager for the works and had an inventive mind. He patented, in 1862, developments of various screw making machines.

Chamberlain & Nettlefold purchased the business of James & Avery in June 1867. A brickworks was built on the eastern part of the site to make bricks for extensions to the plant. A new foundry, annealing shop and carpenter's shop were then constructed. Further extensions were made in about 1875, when new workshops fronting the road were brought into use. The making of hooks, eyes and cotter pins was added to the product range at the same time. A new engine house, erecting shop and offices were added in about 1900.

Wood screws were always made at Kings Norton, but other product lines were manufactured according to demand. Button hooks ceased to be made when their use declined, while the making of tin openers, corkscrews, hat and coat hooks was continued, albeit with better materials. By 1960 the product range at Kings Norton had been extended to include wing nuts, transistor bases, wire rods for washing machines and brake-push rods.

The growth of the GKN Screw Division dates back to when John Sutton Nettlefold founded a factory in Baskerville Place, Birmingham. The main screw factory of the GKN group was built for Chamberlain & Nettlefold in Heath Street between 1852 and 1854.

GKN comprised in the main Guest & Co., Nettlefolds and Watkins & Keen and was a company that was essentially a merger of Midland and South Wales interests. Those in South Wales included iron furnaces, steel works and mines. Mr Lewis had a blast furnace built at Dowlais, near Cardiff in 1758. John Guest became manager of the furnaces in 1760. Three generations of the Guest family were managers of the works until 1815, when J.J. Guest bought the works.

Arthur Keen was born on 23 January 1835 in Cheshire. He joined the LNWR as a goods clerk and eventually was promoted to Goods Agent at Soho station. He met Thomas Astbury, head of Thomas Astbury & Sons, Smethwick Foundry in Rolfe Street. Keen became friendly with the family and married the daughter, Hannah. Keen left the railways and went into business making bolts and nuts for the railways. In 1853 he met an American named Francis Watkins, who worked as a foreman for another firm of bolt makers. They set up as Watkins & Keen at the Victoria Works. In 1858 Thomas Astbury & Son took over part of the London Works, which had been built for Fox Henderson but had become vacant following their bankruptcy. It is believed that Watkins & Keen shared the premises with Thomas Astbury & Son until 1866, when the latter disposed of their interest. In 1864 Watkins & Keen amalgamated with Weston & Grice of West Bromwich and Cwmbran, who made railway fasteners. The result of this merger was a new company called the Patent Nut & Bolt Co. Ltd. A further amalgamation, in July 1900, united the Patent Nut & Bolt with Guest & Co. to form Guest, Keen & Co. Ltd.

John Gerard Colbert, of Marylebone, London took out a patent for 'improvements in making screws' in 1817. He sold his business to John Sutton Nettlefold, an ironmonger from Red Lion Street, Holborn in London. Nettlefold removed the screw manufactory to a water mill at Sunbury on Thames and he was selling screws made there by 1826. In 1842 Nettlefold moved again, this time to steam-powered premises in Broad Street, Birmingham.

Nettlefold negotiated with an American, Thomas J. Sloan, for the purchase of the British patent rights for his wood screw machinery. £30,000 was borrowed from his brother-in-law, Joseph Chamberlain, and part of this deal meant that the Chamberlains joined the partnership. Joseph Chamberlain Snr was, at this time, a wholesaler and boot and shoe manufacturer. Joseph Chamberlain Jnr was appointed works manager for the Broad Street factory.

Screws were made both at the Broad Street factory and at a new factory at Heath Street, in varying sizes from an ounce to 200lb in weight and from the smallest dimensions up to 2ft in length. The iron wire was first cut to required lengths, the head was then formed, and the whole brightened. The nick was then cut in the head by a small machine, the screw pointed and a thread put on it.

Various other companies were brought into the fold. They included James & Avery (1867), Imperial Mills of Sheffield and Hadley (Shropshire) and the Birmingham Screw Co. (established 1868 and taken over by Nettlefolds in 1880). The Heath Street Mill became the largest wood screw mill in the world. These works were rearranged between 1959 and 1965, when the machinery was replaced and improved and faster models installed.

A 1960s exterior view of the Heath Street Works looking towards Cranford Street. (*GKN Magazine*)

Recollections of Mr A. Weare, who joined the company in 1872 and left in 1922 after fifty years' service.
(Book of Recollection, compiled 1927)

The works were started before my knowledge of them, but from what I learnt of the district I conclude they were built on the borders of what was called 'Birmingham Heath'. At that time Heath Street was the main road to the works from town, a hawthorn hedge on the right-hand side extended from Dudley Road to Winson Green Road. This hedge divided the road from a steep bank leading to the feeder. On the left-hand, where St Cuthbert's Church stands was fields and at intervals there were several patches of wasteland, three of these were near to the works. Winson Street was the only street of any importance between Winson Green Road and the Works. I have reason to believe that the whole of this area was in the parish of All Saints, Hockley, and that the mission room opposite Tudor Street was served by the clergy of that church. There was a small Methodist chapel near Swingler's coal yard. A small post office in a cottage at the top of Lodge Road, described by the postal authorities as the Birmingham Heath office, served the district. Dudley Road was like a village street. There were three large houses – 'Summerfield', 'Bellefield' and a house now occupied by Dr Alldridge, a farm (Fawdry's Farm), which extended from Summerfield Park to Rotton Park Road (the farmhouse and outbuildings occupied the land between where Lloyds Bank stands and Summerfield Park), a number of small villas, public houses and a few shops. I have seen cornfields close to the road opposite Winson Street. The Institute erected by the firm in Winson Street for the use of their employees was standing, but derelict. I was told that most of the workers lived too far away to be able to take advantage of its benefits. (There were no 'buses or trams running that way in those days).

The main entrance to the Works was in Hope Street (a short street leading to an arm of the canal) containing a large public house on the corner and two or three cottages faced by a large plot of waste land. The entrance was at the canal end. The time office was on the left and the Blacksmith's and Millwright's Shop on the right. A few yards away stood the screw mill and its accessories, these being in Smethwick. The business of the firm had increased considerably in consequence of the Franco-German War, and a short time before I became an employee a large warehouse had been built, as the need for the premises used for warehouse and office purposes was urgently wanted for manufacturing purpose.

The working conditions were for many years, to put it mildly 'crude'. Wages were low. There was no organization for the provision of meals, or separate rooms in which to take them, neither was there any provision for the hanging up of outer garments (no cloak rooms). The sanitary arrangements were deplorable, but I believe quite as good as those obtaining in other factories at the time. The time worked in the Mill, Fitting Shop etc was 54 hours per week and nominally 48 hours in the Order Warehouse, but the workers in the latter were often called upon to work after six o'clock to despatch goods for export in order to catch vessels.

Banks of screw-making machines fill the cavernous space of the screw mill buildings at Heath Street. *(GKN Magazine)*

Below: Aerial view of the Heath Street factory, located at the boundary between Smethwick and Birmingham. *(GKN Magazine)*

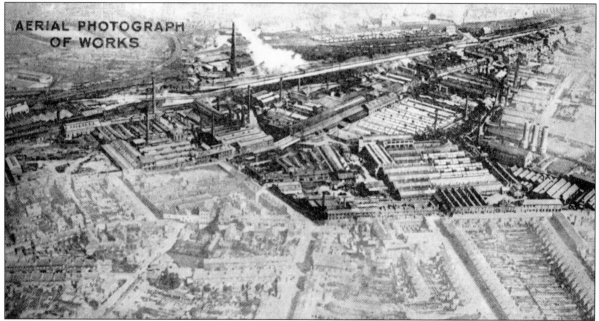

By 1960 the modernised Heath Street factory employed 4,700 people in making wood screws and other products such as push rods. Cold forming techniques enabled screws to be turned from metal bar and nuts pressed from sheet strip.

The United Wire Works at Adderley Street supplied brass wire to the GKN Group for the production of brass screws. The roots of this company began in Glasgow, where William McMurray, wire weaver, made various domestic articles such as fireguards and wire cloth for paper making. The Birmingham wire works began as an offshoot of the Scottish company during the First World War. The Adderley Park mills were started in 1916. Their principal object was to supply Foudrinier wire to be woven into wire mesh for making paper. Peacetime production from 1919 was increased to included brass wire for screw making. GKN were keen to retain this supply and from 1922 set up United Wire Works (Birmingham) Ltd. They initially had a half-share, but six years later, in July 1928, GKN took complete control of this company.

Production of brass and phosphor bronze wire and rod was stepped up and adjacent premises were acquired to permit works extensions. Production was carried out using the traditional methods of casting brass into bars, rolling and then drawing to the required thickness. Methods changed with the decision taken in 1939 to install an extrusion press. The 1,250-ton press, installed in 1941, produced brass rod for GKN. The new machine increased production and proved to be an invaluable asset to meet the unprecedented demands for rod and wire, which were made during the war. Even though this press produced extruded material in straight lengths, Harry Lowdnes, managing director, devised a machine to coil the wire rods as they left the press.

During 1945 GKN commenced a three-year modernisation of the United Wire Works. Multi-die and continuous drawing machines replaced the old-style bench-block drawing machines. The GKN board also approved the building of a new casting shop when a half-ton capacity electric melting furnace was installed, along with a new tandem mill and an 18-inch rolling mill. A disused retort house which had belonged to Birmingham Gas Department was purchased and converted, and used to house a second extrusion press. The Wire Works now occupied a 3-acre site.

Further works expansion was commenced in 1957 when factory land in Glover Street, covering another 2 acres, was taken and adapted for a new wire rod mill. The new mill was completed during 1961 and was fitted out to modern style of production, where raw material entered at one end and the finished product was delivered at the other. The long building housed a gas-fired continuous casting furnace and a 2,500-ton extrusion press. A conveyor system was installed for moving coils of wire along the building to the draw-benches or transport department for despatch by road.

NAIL & RIVET MAKING

Nails were made from different metals and alloys. They might be made from wire or cut from sheet metal. Copper nails and rivets were particularly favoured by ship and boat builders as no other metal had been found that resisted the corrosive action of sea water.

Nail making was long established throughout the Birmingham and Black Country district, where nail rods were cut to size and shape by families of nailworkers. It was a trade that faced severe competition from the cut-nail trade and mechanisation in general from 1850 onward.

The Mitre Works, Eyre Street *(Kynoch Journal)*

The cut-nail mill, a commodious building, partially glass roofed and well ventilated, is occupied by a large number of the latest automatic machines. Each of these is in the charge of a female hand whose chief duty is to feed the machine with strips of metal, which, after passing through the mill are ejected on the opposite side into a receptacle arranged for the purpose. The machine not only cuts nails, but in addition forms the head, so that when the article leaves the interior workings a perfect nail is the result.

Another department, the wire nail mill exhibits much the same conditions of things. The main characteristic of the whole building being the display of all the latest machinery and appliances necessary for the manufacturing nails of the highest quality. Since Kynoch Limited have added Eyre Street to their other establishments, arrangements have been made whereby a considerably increased output can be available to meet the requirements of the various customers. At the present time something like one hundred tons of nails are produced weekly, and these are sent to all quarters of the globe.

From *The Gentleman's Journal and Gentlewomen's Court Review* (29 October 1910)

A visit to Messr. David Powis & Sons, Copper, Nail & Rivet Works, Floodgate Street, Birmingham, is an object lesson, proving the enormous amount of copper used in the industry alone. Powis and Sons manufacture from the small cut copper tack up to the seventeen-inch copper nail. At one time, the standard for the length of nails was the height in piles of pennies, and the nail received its designation from the piles of pennies that its height equalled, hence the derivation of the name that still survives in the trade, 'Tenpenny nail'; but after alteration in the coinage of the old copper penny, this standard gave way to the more rational one of inch measure. The variety of copper nails used in boat-building itself, is confusing to the amateur; in one of Powis and Sons' Store-rooms, with a capacity of 30 tons weight of material, we noticed the following varieties of Boat nails alone: Rose head, counter-sunk head, Rose head flat point, Deck head flat point, corrugated copper sheathing tacks; beside copper boat roves, rivets and washers.

It is a pleasant and instructive experience to walk through Powis & Son's Copper nail factory, but it is impossible to describe the multitudinous and intricate machines in use, and as laymen our attempt would only weary the reader, but these machines seem to anything but talk. Nails, tacks, brads, rivets, and washers come tumbling out into receptacles by the millions. Metal is cut, punched and treated in a very inconsiderate manner, but always with the ultimate result of emerging from the ordeal elegantly shaped, and ready for a useful life. From this the nails are conveyed to the polishing room, and placed in revolving barrels, from which they eventually make their exit like refined gold, bright, shining and ready for delivery. It is very agreeable to see in Powis and Sons factory all the employees especially the females, so neat, clean and respectable looking; the labour is so perfunctory, merely feeding the machines, there is not the usual hurry and bustle noticeable in some factories, nor is there the usual dirt and filth; the warehouse with the spruce girls wrapping the various goods, for consignments to the packers. Is quite a picture of cleanliness and order.

An important maker of cut-nails was the Mitre Works in Eyre Street, Spring Hill. Thomas Hadley started the firm in Bishop Street, near to the Mitre Inn. Felix Hadley, iron merchant, later assisted him and the firm traded as Hadley Brothers for a number of years. The move to Eyre Street was made during the 1860s, when they established a new cut-nail factory on land next to Glyndon & Shorthouse's Metal Rolling Mills. They later traded as Felix Hadley & Co. Arthur Chamberlain became chairman of Felix Hadley & Co. Ltd in 1894 and shortly afterwards the adjacent firm of B. & G. Shorthouse, Metal Rollers, was amalgamated. The whole of the works of metal rolling and nail making were concentrated within one large building. The improvements paved the way for the takeover of the firm by Kynoch Ltd.

The core business of Kynoch Ltd was the making of ammunition, but George Kynoch had built up a supply chain of other trades that included metal rolling. The metal trades were essential for the supply of brass for cartridge making. Kynoch Ltd was formed in 1884 and George then decided to devote time to politics and other causes. He became MP for Aston and was also chairman for Aston Villa Football Club. These varied occupations left less time for Kynoch's, and trade suffered. The shareholders' tolerance was short lived. A committee was formed to investigate the problems in 1888. Their findings proved unfavourable for George Kynoch. He resigned from the board and left the country to live in South Africa. His popular choice replacement was Arthur Chamberlain. The Chamberlains were no strangers to politics either, but Arthur was a dedicated industrialist. He turned the finances of Kynoch's around and set about making further business acquisitions to bolster the firm's activities, many of which are described in *Birmingham's Industrial Heritage*. Kynoch's produced a wide range of different nails under 'Mitre' brand from brass, iron and steel. These included cut-nails, clasp, clout, cone-head roofing nails, wire slate nails, patent twisted wire nails, wire staples, wire hooks, shoe nails, patent steel dog spikes, brass-head picture nails, tram rails and gas pipe hooks. Brass picture hooks were a particular speciality.

A portion of the Eyre Street Factory when in the ownership of Felix Hadley & Co., *c.* 1900. *(Kynoch Journal)*

The impressive frontage of the Eyre Street factory buildings, April 2001. Originally associated with the cut-nail trade, this group of buildings was later occupied by Albert Phillips, and as the Excelsior Works was adapted for the making of metallic bedsteads. *(Ray Shill)*

Eyre Street, April 2001. The essential fabric of the Felix Hadley factory has been retained to the present day, although the central section which appears in the 1900 photograph has disappeared. *(Ray Shill)*

Arthur Chamberlain died in 1913, and was succeeded by his son Arthur in the management of Kynoch's. These were changing times and consolidation, rather than independence, became the chosen route for many industries. Kynoch Ltd became part of Nobel Industries Ltd in 1918. A programme of rationalisation was introduced and certain parts of the company were closed down and the buildings disposed of. One casualty was the Mitre Works, which shut down about this time. The Mitre Works by then occupied a long frontage to the north side of Eyre Street and there were also buildings on the other side of the street. The metal rollers William West & Son Ltd took part of the site.

UMBRELLA RIB MANUFACTURE

Umbrella making was established in Birmingham during the nineteenth century and was able to draw on the local metal-making skills. Umbrella parts and components comprised a metal framework covered with cloth or oiled silk, while the handles were made from agate, bamboo, bone, horn, ivory or wood. The metal parts were commonly described as umbrella furniture and included elements of brass, copper, iron and steel. Birmingham manufacturers specialised in the making of umbrella furniture and ribs. The making of ribs proved to be a lucrative venture for those firms who chose to undertake it, and a select group of makers came to be established in Birmingham, principally from 1870 onwards.

Steel wire was brought from Sheffield to be made into ribs, although some steel was made locally. Thomas Cox & Sons were steel converters and refiners at the Premier Steel Works, located on the corner of Green Street and Alcester Street, where crinoline wire and umbrella ribs were produced. Thomas Cox became Cox Brothers & Holland, and by 1880 had relocated to new premises at Percy Road, Greet where umbrella furniture became the principal product.

Corder & Turley built up a successful rib trade at their factory in Allison Street on the corner of Well Lane. Corder & Turley's works were equipped with japanning shops, hardening shops, forking shops, runner shops and riveting shops that were required for

The former umbrella rib factory, Allison Street, which was built for Corder & Turley to the designs of architect James Moffat, 1998. *(Ray Shill)*

the making of the principal components of the umbrella trade. Such were the profits of the trade that this factory was rebuilt to the designs of the eminent Birmingham architect, James Moffat.

Other factories included the Armstrong and Salop Works. Henry Holland & Co. had a factory in Salop Street, Highgate Park, known as the Salop Works, while William Bindley and William Gell owned the Armstrong Works, Chester Street. Bindley and Gell commenced business together in 1880, trading from premises in Newhall Hill before setting up the Chester Street works. Supply of quality steel was the key to success in the trade, and in 1898 Bindley and Gell secured a stronger future through the merger with Crownshaw, Chapman & Co., owners of the North British Works and River Don Saw Works and makers of steel, saws, tools and wire at Penistone Road, Sheffield. Joseph Wright, then owner of the Sheffield works, gave his name to the newly formed firm, Wright, Bindley & Gell, when this company was finally registered in February 1899.

The formation of Wright, Bindley & Gell was soon accompanied by the acquisition of Corder & Turley's business in Allison Street. Further takeovers followed in 1902 with the acquisition of the firms of Cox Brothers & Holland and Henry Holland & Co. The Salop Works had for some time been unconnected with the Holland name, but were run by the Corah Brothers. John Corah used a portion of his profits of the sale to invest in Davenports C.B. Brewery Ltd and became a director of that concern. Thus it was that the umbrella trade in Birmingham was brought together under the control of one major manufacturer.

WIRE ROPE

The making of wire rope was developed during the nineteenth century to supply cable for the telegraph and rope for haulage purposes. An important market developed for the supply of wire ropes for collieries and other mines, where ropes were used to raise cages or incorporated into endless rope or main and tail rope haulage systems. Principal Birmingham makers were Webster & Horsfall, Latch & Batchelor and John & Edwin Wright.

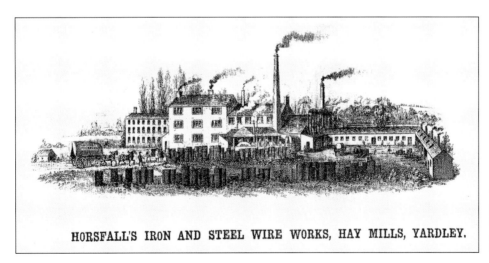

HORSFALL'S IRON AND STEEL WIRE WORKS, HAY MILLS, YARDLEY.

This 1853 engraving published in *Cornish's Guide* shows the Webster & Horsfall Iron and Steel Wire Works, Hay Mills.

John & Edwin Wright made twine and metallic ropes. They were originally engaged in the hemp and twine rope trade at Dartmouth Street and ropery at Water Street. It was a trade that had formerly been carried out by their mother Ann, but following her death the business had passed to the two brothers. Their business was transferred to a new rope works in Garrison Street during the 1860s and remained there for some hundred years.

CHAPTER THREE

THE BRASS TRADE

Birmingham's industrial success was built on the shoulders of the brass trade. The working of this metal developed into many different occupations and to this day remains an important manufacturing trade in the city.

Brass is an alloy of copper and zinc, made in different proportions of each metal to suit particular needs. In the eighteenth and early nineteenth centuries it was made at local 'Brass houses' through the combination of copper and calamine. The chief sources of copper included Macclesfield, Bristol and later Swansea, while calamine was brought from Derbyshire. This method of making brass was both time-consuming and inefficient and was superseded by the direct combination of copper with spelter (metallic zinc).

William Hutton, historian, recorded that the first Birmingham brass house was Turner's in Coleshill Street. William Turner made a limited amount of brass there during the eighteenth century. When the Birmingham Canal was constructed, transport of brass and copper into the town was considerably improved. Three canal-side brass houses (at Broad Street, Spon Lane and Smethwick) were constructed during the 1780s and '90s,

Over the roof tops – an engraving of Birmingham showing the annealing furnace towers of Turner's brassworks, Coleshill Street. (From the South East Prospect of Birmingham, 1752)

which came to supply calamine brass to local brass founders and workers. Brass also came into the district by the boatload, supplied by the Bristol-based brass houses such as John Freeman.

By the year 1833 all local brass houses had ceased making brass by the calamine method. British copper supplied by the Swansea Copper Works continued to be the mainstay of local brass production throughout the nineteenth century. Copper in ingots or slabs would be carried by rail or boat to serve the many foundries and works. By 1910 the sources of both metals for Birmingham brass workers were chiefly obtained from abroad. Copper came from Spain, Japan and the USA, while Belgium sent spelter. The mixing of copper and zinc might also include small percentages of tin, lead or nickel. Brass was but one of a range of copper alloys, others being Argentite, Potosi Silver, Delta Metal, Silveroid, Muntz Metal and White Brass.

Brass made by the calamine method was a limited supply compared to the later years when copper and zinc were mixed together. Yet the skill of the brass worker was able to produce an article that was prized for its colour. Brass was often chosen for decorative work. Yellows and golds were often enhanced through coverings of varnish. A fine kind of brass made to imitate gold was known as ormolu, and this metal was frequently prized as a decoration for, or inlay into, furniture.

Some Brass Alloys				
Trade Name	Copper %	Zinc %	Lead %	Tin %
Brazing or hard solder	50	50		
Extrusion Brass	55	45		
Muntz Metal	60	40		
Baggage Check Brass	62	38		
Clock Brass (for clock wheels and frames)	62–64½	37–39½	2½–3	
Cutlery Brass (for knife linings)	63	37		
Bell Metal	64½–65	34½–35		¾
Common Brass and Pin Wire	65	35		
Drawing Brass and Dipping Brass	66	34		
Watch Brass	66–68	30–32	2	
Clock case metal	68	32		
Balance Beams for clocks	68–70	28–30	2	
Cartridge Brass	70	30		
Spring Brass	72	28		
Spring Brass (extra quality)	75	25		1
Common Brass	80	20		
Pen Metal	85	13		2
Medal Metal	86	14		
Medal Metal (rich colour)	95–97	1–3		2
Leaded Bronze	87–88	11–12	1	
Bronze	87–88	11–12		1
Best Bronze (Goldine)	90	10		
Chain and Optical Bronze	90–98			2–10
Percussion Cap gilding	95	5		

Once spelter became available to the brass caster, a whole range of alloy combinations became possible. It soon became clear that different percentages of copper and zinc alloys were suited for different purposes. Even mixtures were used as solder, but as the percentage of copper was increased several useful metals were formed. These included the varied alloys for clock and watch manufacture and the general and common brasses that were adapted by the skill of the founder into a host of different articles.

When brass was cast, it was produced in rectangular-shaped pieces sometimes known as strips, but more frequently as bars or ingots. Strip casting was the name given to the combination of spelter and copper in crucibles and the pouring of molten metal into moulds. The principal caster was muffled to avoid inhaling the fumes. Ingots of brass were then either re-melted to be shaped in the mould or heated sufficiently to pass through rolls to produce sheet brass, or through a die to make wire. Foundry work, rolling and drawing were key elements in the brass-working trade. From the rolling mill brass went to the stamper or die sinker to be fashioned into shape. These basic processes were adopted in a variety of forms to suit a range of customers:

Art metal and embossed (repoussé) work	Railway brass founders
Bedsteads (brass and iron)	Rolled metal manufacturers
Bell founders	Naval brass founders
Buttons, badges, medals, military and naval ornament makers	Nails, rivets, bolts and nuts
Cabinet brass founders	Specialist brass work
Carriage and other lamps	Spinners and other lathe work
Chandelier, gas and electrical fittings	Stamped brass foundry and brass stampers
Engineers' and plumbers' brass founders	Tube manufacturers (brass and cased tube)
Harness and saddle ironmongery	Wire drawers, wire workers, pin makers and brass chain workers

The diversity and specialist work carried out by some Birmingham brass workers are best summed up by the following account written by Richard Keates:

A Short Account of the Birmingham Brass Trade (*The Metal Industry*, June 1910)

One firm will manufacture nothing but shop fittings; another would not entertain any business but that in mandrel-drawn tubes of the lightest gauge and the smallest diameter for pencil cases etc; while yet another would courteously but firmly direct you to another address for water fittings suitable for the South American markets, making only the heavier and more expensive varieties themselves. And so the trade has been divided and sub divided with its varied interests until it has arrived at its extraordinary position today. A vast unwieldy industry, employing at least 50,000 hands, from the humble moulder and girl core maker and 'dogger-up' to the typist or designer and manager, and turning out annually a value at what a conservative estimate puts at five million pounds sterling. And as yet, it is practically unprotected.

It is curious to contemplate the enormous amount of energy put forth individually, by the multitude of small firms in Birmingham; each striving (and in the majority of cases succeeding) to pay its way and all feeling the competition keenly.

Cartland's Lacquering & Zaponing Hall. The task of covering brass with lacquer was generally considered a female occupation. At Cartland's, female workers are seen applying lacquers such as Zapon to brass articles. *(Birmingham Arts & Industry Magazine)*

Where the brass was cast. The two-storey brass foundry was located to the rear of the works by the railway. This carefully posed photograph shows various brass workers going about their duties. *(Birmingham Arts & Industry Magazine)*

The frontage of Cartland Brassworks, Constitution Hill, reflects the fortune some brass workers might achieve. This firm was engaged in the art metal trade, where special attention was given to the ornamentation, quality and style of the piece. This group of buildings included offices and showrooms. *(Birmingham Arts & Industry Magazine)*

Birmingham brass workers practised all or some of the key brass working processes. Firms like R.W. Winfield, at Cambridge Street, had an extensive works that had foundries, rolling and wire mills and were engaged in many aspects of the brass trade. Others confined themselves to specific markets. Many carried out work in cramped and restricted premises. Vices, benches, presses, stamps and lathes crammed into tight factory spaces was a common Birmingham sight and provided regular employment for the brass workers who fashioned rough castings or brass sheet into a useful product.

THE BRASS FOUNDERS

The process of brass working was a long-established and staple trade in Birmingham. Many brass founders restricted their activities to the making of rough work, which was the name given to the state of the castings when they came from the mould. Rough work from the foundry was sold to the finishers, who smoothed and polished the product ready for use or sale.

Castings were made in many shapes and sizes, but every single piece began with a design made on paper, which was then reproduced in wood, or wax, by the modeller. A mould of the model was cast in lead, which was then checked by the chaser, who repaired all deficiencies before a master model was cast from the lead mould in brass. This brass model was handed over to the casters, whose job was to reproduce the image in fine sand held in an iron box, and duplicate the model as often as needed. The model was firmly indented in wet sand and once the impression was made the model was withdrawn. A channel in the sand, called the gate, was made to admit the molten brass into the sand box and fill up the space. The mould was then allowed to cool and the casting was then removed from the box. Another workman then dressed the casting to remove some of the rough edges.

Both men and boys were employed in the casting shop. The boys' work chiefly involved the preparation of moulds and cores, pounding, shaking on, or generally helping the men in tasks such as stirring the metal in the furnace and skimming the pots of molten brass before they were poured. Work in the brass foundry was an unhealthy occupation, as well as being a very dirty one. There was a considerable amount of dust, and workers were exposed to the noxious zinc fumes given off from the molten and flaming mixture. When brass was poured from the pots into the moulds the whole casting shop would be filled with fumes and clouds of white flakes that would settle all about, on clothes, walls and the floor.

Early brass founders included Benjamin Cook of Caroline Street, who was quite an inventive individual. During 1811 Thomas Attwood and Benjamin Cook were granted a patent that formed the basis of the cased tube industry and the development of many items of ornamental items of furniture. Cook's and Attwood's patent no. 3,609 of 1812 confirmed and improved the method for making window blinds, fire screens, chimney pieces, sashes, door, picture frames and frames dressing, pier and other glasses and various useful and ornamental items. Cased rods as per Cook's and Attwood's patent were used to make external frames of venetian or parlour window blinds, window sashes of solid rods or tubes, window frames of iron or wood, also cornice poles, external ribs of carriage wheels, and to form bedsteads. In fact, it was the cased rod that assisted the Birmingham bedstead trade, which will be discussed in Chapter 4.

Foundry brass works supplied a variety of needs that ranged from the domestic to the naval and military. Domestic and household brass work comprised a variety of different items that ranged from castings for brass bedsteads, balustrades, fire-irons, curtain rods, cornice poles, picture frames, gas-fittings and lamps. The Birmingham brass founders made gas-fittings in large quantities, which ranged in quality from the plain to the ornate. Naval brass foundry was concerned with all brass work used in ships and required great care in its production. The military work consisted of the making of sword handles, gun furniture, studs for harness and the various pieces of brass that made up a soldier's equipment.

Most items were coated in lacquer, which gave a protective finish to the brass. Women and girls were commonly employed in the lacquer shops. A variety of varnishes or japans might be used to create a specific surface or effect. Before dipping tanks were invented these were painted on, and each item was usually placed in a stove to bake the surface coating.

Robert Walter Winfield, born April 1799, was the third son of John and Mary Winfield. His father died when he was young and his mother looked after him until he was of an age to go to work. Winfield's first job was working for Benjamin Cook, and it was during this time that he gained the skills which equipped him for a successful career in the brass trade. Winfield commenced business on his own account at the Crescent, beside Gibson's Canal Arm, in 1820. Various extensions were made to the premises during the 1830s and the adjacent Union rolling mills were acquired when they came up for sale. Winfield's works came to occupy some 2 acres of ground and to have five separate departments: metal rolling mills, gas fitting (including chandeliers, lamps and chimney stands), bedsteads and portable bedsteads, general brass foundry and carpentry at the canal wharf for making of packing cases.

Winfield adopted many new techniques. These included brass foundry stamping processes that made cornices, cornice poles and curtain bands. Purity of colour was achieved by dipping in lacquer made on the premises. He embarked on the making of brass and copper tubing, gas fittings and chandeliers, bedsteads, ships' fittings and architectural ornaments. Winfield also made brass and copper wire and had a coal merchant's business at a nearby wharf on the Oozells Loop. Winfield's continued with their wide product range throughout the nineteenth century, until a fall-off in trade led to the receivers being called in. The works were offered for sale in 1897 and sections were sold off, but the core metal rolling business was retained.

Thomas Messenger started an equally long-lived business. His brass foundry lay close to Winfield's works and faced Broad Street. Messenger & Sons produced high quality brassware that included chandeliers, candelabra and gas fittings in bronze and ormolu. They also produced railway signal and carriage roof lamps, as other carriage fittings. They remained in Broad Street until 1935, when the buildings were demolished to make room for the ill-fated Civic Centre Scheme.

The Chamberlain family was another name that was associated with the brass trade, through Arthur and Neville Chamberlain's business interests. Neville Chamberlain, better known for his life in politics, gave important service to Birmingham industry both with Elliot's Metals at Selly Oak and ships' berths makers Hoskins & Son at Bordesley. Arthur Chamberlain, who was uncle to Neville, by contrast, devoted less time to politics, but had an immense impact on Birmingham industry.

Arthur Chamberlain was born in 1842. He was the third son of Joseph Chamberlain, a cordwainer of London. He came to Birmingham, with the rest of the family, when his father became a partner in the firm of Nettlefold & Chamberlain. Arthur was educated with brothers Joseph and Richard at University College School, London. Arthur and Richard went into business with Henry Smith as brass

Messenger & Sons had a brass works and showrooms in Broad Street until the mid-1930s. It produced quality art metal work for gas and electric light fittings, bedsteads and a variety of other domestic items. The above shows a variety of lamp fittings put together for the International Exhibition. *(Kelly's Directory of Birmingham, 1879)*

MESSENGER & SONS' CASE IN THE INTERNATIONAL EXHIBITION.

founders in New Bartholomew Street. While brother Joseph followed his destiny with a political career, Arthur seemed content to pursue a career in industry. Following the death of Smith, the two brothers continued to trade in the foundry business. Arthur also went into partnership with George Hookham, as electric light engineers, and developed a large trade in electric dynamos and electric lighting accessories at the New Bartholomew Street plant. This firm also carried out contracts to install public lighting. Arthur Chamberlain, such was his business acumen, developed wider interests in industry, which included the chairmanship of Kynochs and Tubes Ltd. His political achievements were less than those of his famous brother, Joseph, but he was elected town councillor in 1872, and assisted both brothers in the organisation of the Liberal Unionist Party.

The designer's, modeller's and pattern maker's skill was essential to making of moulds and cores for brass foundry work. A great variety of shapes and forms was required, but many founders could keep only a limited supply. It thus became a feature of the trade that brass founders would specialise in certain lines or products.

Edwards Brothers were art metal workers and produced decorative candlesticks and similar ware. They also supplied standard brass foundry work for the gas industry. Company records for the 1920s and 1930s mention the supply of gas works, pendants and also glass bowls to Sheffield gas works, light fittings and table stands to Sevenoaks and District Electricity Co., brass adaptors to Newcastle Gas Co., Ox Copper pendants to York Gas Co., wired lights to the Electric Wire and Repair Co., steel bronze pendants to Bath Gas Co., Ox Copper brackets to the Darlington Gas Co., Grimsby Gas Co., Liverpool Gas Co. and the Shrewsbury Gas Co.

The firm of Edwards Brothers was formed in the early 1890s when George Edwards decided to set up in business on his own account in premises at Charles Henry Street. George, it seems, learned his trade at R.W. Winfield, Cambridge Street, where his father, George Thomas Edwards, was employed as an engine fitter and later as an engineer. According to the 1881 census the young George was employed, aged 15, as a brass dresser, while elder sister Emily worked as a lacquerer. Quite possibly both Emily and George also worked at Winfields, which was then among Birmingham's most prominent brass manufacturers and had a reputation for the manufacture of top quality art metal work.

The changes within the firm of Winfields had led to a gradual reduction on their commitments in the brass foundry and art metal trades, following the creation of Winfields Ltd at the end of 1886. Their subsequent policies ultimately led to the piecemeal sale of all departments with the exception of the rolling mills, where George Thomas Edwards was evidently employed.

Strip casting at R.W. Winfields' works, Cambridge Street. A. Morrow produced several drawings that showed various jobs undertaken at Winfields'. In this view workers are shown mixing molten copper and zinc. Morrow has captured the moment through artistic use of light and dark.

A job with Winfields in the art metal trade would seem to hold little prospect for any young and ambitious workers, and these factors may well have influenced the course of action taken by George Edwards. Younger brother William came to assist George, and by 1894 both George and William were trading as art metal morkers at 23 and 25 Emily Street. In 1895 larger premises in Rea Street were leased from Reuben Shipway. George Tonks had formerly used these buildings for the brass trade. In 1898 their father, George Thomas Edwards, arranged for the purchase of the lease from Shipway for 63, 64 and 65 Rea Street. Edwards Brothers had become a truly family concern, with both father and sons involved. The firm remained at Rea Street for eight years before moving again to larger premises at the Sampson Works, Sampson Road North.

The Sampson Road Works had been built as a bedstead factory for the Birmingham Bedstead Co. during 1886. After the business went into receivership in 1893, the factory was taken over by R.F. Hall Cycle Component Manufacturers and was briefly owned by the Cycle Component Manufacturing Co. Ltd, before work was concentrated at their Selly Oak factory. The premises then passed to the Rippingille Brothers, iron founders, and were sub-let to the Birmingham Advertising Tablet Co. until 1901 or 1902, before they moved to new works in Smethwick. During 1903 Edwards Brothers acquired the Sampson Works, which became the home of the firm for another thirty years. William Edwards' association with the company ended during the early 1930s and George Edwards and his family gained complete control of the company. By 1933 the business was relocated to 56–60 Hockley Street, where the firm remained until closure.

Another important aspect of the brass foundry trade was the supply of plumbing articles for domestic or industrial use. Samuel Booth & Co. Ltd was formed in 1914 to take over assets of the business of manufacture and dealing in sanitary brassware, valves, gas fittings and electric light fittings carried on by J. Booth, as Samuel Booth & Co. This firm, which could trace its origins back to 1850, was a long-term supplier of this equipment and still advertises the sale of Victorian-style bathroom equipment from their Cheapside address.

STAMPED BRASS FOUNDRY WORK

The key task of taking brass ingots and rolling them into sheet or a strip of metal enabled the fashioning of the metal to specific shapes with the use of a die stamp or hand press. The process was already established at the start of the nineteenth century, when William Bird & Co. made military ornaments, looking glasses and picture frames at Nechells Mills and sold them from a warehouse in Great Charles Street.

Stamping produced a wide range of products. These included the knobs and panels for bedstead makers, brackets, doorplates and fingerplates. Chandelier and lamp makers had chains, globe holders, lamp fittings, lamp plates, lamp stands, brass work for the electroplater, art brasses, ash trays, butter dishes, electrical stampings and fender makers' brass work, fancy brass foundry for jewellers, beading wire, gallery borders, beads, jewel case fittings, fastenings, pins and rivets.

A host of companies were engaged in the stamped brass foundry trade. They included John Wathen of Globe Works, Barford Street, which produced lamps. J. Hudson's Metropolitan Brass Foundry made gas fittings and military ornaments; S. Heath & Sons Ltd, Cobden Works, Leopold Street, made bedstead fittings; Jones, Price & Co. steam stamping works produced chandeliers and harness furniture; while Bodill Parker produced a range of furniture articles.

Bodill Parker owned the Albion Works, Great Hampton Street. George Bodill established this business in 1860s. He took over the business of James Edward Harrison at 35 and 36 Great Hampton Row. They made brass curtain rings for bamboo curtain rods, and brass bedstead knobs. In 1882 William Bodill and William Bodill Parker Jnr formed Bodill Parker & Co. Adjacent premises were purchased and production increased. The firm supplied wood struts for aircraft and stampings for the Ministry of Munitions during the First World War. Production was hampered following a serious fire, but the works were rebuilt. The disruption reduced what might have been lucrative profits.

When the war ended and the recession set in the company suffered financially and was wound up. A group of workers purchased the factory and restarted production, using the original name. They absorbed G. Brown, garden syringe manufacturer of 52 New John Street. Production in the 1920s included general brass foundry, eyelets, grommets, ships' thimbles, garden syringes and hose fittings. Thimbles were brass rings

The Beacon Works, Hampton Street, which belonged to Smith & Davis, produced stamped brass foundry products. *(Smith & Davis Magazine)*

Left: Beacon Bert was a character made up of cast and stamped brass parts to illustrate the variety of products made by Smith & Davis. *(Smith & Davis Magazine)*

The May & Padmore Factory, Tyseley, produced brass pressings for the motor trade, cabinet makers, ship builders and for use in various architectural metal work to ornament buildings. *(Birmingham Chamber of Commerce Journal, 1920)*

for ropes, and were supplied to ship owners and sail makers. Some were also supplied for airship use. This firm continued to be profitable and moved to larger premises in Lower Tower Street during 1960.

Frederick Smith and Frank Davis founded the firm of Smith & Davis, stamped brass founders, in 1901. Their first works were located in Essington Street. New premises were purchased during 1909 and a new factory in Hampton Street. This works became known as Beacon Works, as was their trademark. They executed various orders for government offices during the First World War, and built up considerable business after 1920. They became large consumers of rolled brass, which was worked up through stamping into a variety of products. These included door stops, door knobs, picture hooks, candle holders, curtain rings, draw pulls, brass numbers, bolts, brass name plates, and stair eyes. The firm were keen to bring out new product ranges, and by 1927 were making double-stamped hinges to several designs. In 1930 they introduced a new style of curtain rod to their range, and to keep up with demand made new works extensions from time to time. Those built during 1930 provided additional manufacturing space, a new lacquering department and metal stores. Further extension along Henrietta Street and Hospital Street were finished before 1939. Smith & Davis left Birmingham eleven years later, when production was transferred to a new factory in Friars Park Road, Wednesbury.

May & Padmore came to specialise in hot brass pressings for the motor trade. Their works in Leopold Street were transferred to a new factory in Wharfdale Road, Tyseley, in about 1920. In addition to supplying the motor industry they also supplied cabinet brass foundry and architectural metal work.

OUR NEW FACTORY AT TYSELEY, BIRMINGHAM.

VARIETY IN THE BRASS TRADE

The list of brass products was almost endless. Herbert Pargeter & Co., of Dean Street, specialised in small ware using saw piercing in brass or other non-ferrous metals to make fish covers, monograms and ornaments. Frederick Whitfield & Co., Oxford Street and Samuel Mason, Dale End made components for beer engines. George Glydon, Colmore Works, Oozells Street, made garden engines, hose pipe fittings and syringes.

Some firms specialised in making 'toys' and novelties. These included hooks, barometer fittings, bookmarks, camera parts, clock fittings, parts for corsetry, hat ornaments, paper fasteners, paper knives and other stationery items, umbrella fasteners and rings. W.H. Walker & G. Walker made clock fittings at the Victor Works, Angelina Street. S. Bagnall & Co., Bradford Street, made ticket fasteners, while G. Bentley & Co. constructed perambulator fittings at Ellen Street and W.H. Deakin made barometer fittings in Hampton Street.

George Tucker produced eyelets and sail thimbles at their Dartmouth Street Works (and still make fasteners at their works, which are now located at Perry Barr). Thomas Westwood manufactured stair rods at the Moreville Street Works, and Cope Allman did the same at the Unity Tube Works. Cope Allman were also an important supplier of cased tubing to the bedstead trade. C.M. Powell, Aston Road, produced brass furniture, coal vase mounts, japan ware, pianoforte furniture and hinges. Charles Winn & Co. of St Thomas Works, Granville Street produced work for the engineering trade, which included gauges, gas governors and steam gauges.

In later years the name of Benton & Stone was associated with the supply of lubricants to the motor trade, but previous to this their Bracebridge Street factory manufactured bells. Their range included dinner, office call and tea bells. Hudson & Spencer of the Alexander works, Caroline Street, produced call, alarm, door and cycle bells. John Charles Tonks, Lancaster Street produced brass knobs and screws, ash pan, drawer and range knobs. Wednesbury tube maker John Russell had a brass works in Birmingham, the Belmont Chandelier works, where bracket fittings for the gas and electric industry were made. Brass cocks and valves for beer engines, water pipes and other sanitary fittings were produced at the Paragon works, Hampton Street, which belonged to John Walford.

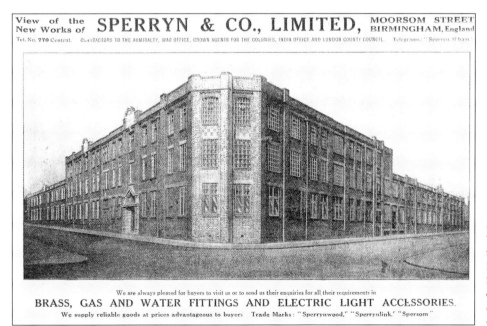

View of the New Works of **SPERRYN & CO., LIMITED,** MOORSOM STREET BIRMINGHAM, England

Tel. No. 770 Central.   CONTRACTORS TO THE ADMIRALTY, WAR OFFICE, CROWN AGENTS FOR THE COLONIES, INDIA OFFICE AND LONDON COUNTY COUNCIL.   Telegrams: "Sperryn, B'ham"

We are always pleased for buyers to visit us or to send us their enquiries for all their requirements in

BRASS, GAS AND WATER FITTINGS AND ELECTRIC LIGHT ACCESSORIES.

We supply reliable goods at prices advantageous to buyers   Trade Marks : "Sperrynwood," "Sperrynlink," "Spersom"

Many Birmingham brass founders engaged in the supply of domestic items. Sperryn & Co., Moorsom Street, produced a comprehensive range. (*Birmingham Chamber of Commerce Journal*)

Bronze was an alloy of copper and tin. The Phosphor Bronze Co. had various factories in Birmingham. In this 1950s view the frontage of the factory in Digbeth can be seen to the right. The view shows Digbeth High Street before the road was widened. *(Local Studies Department, Birmingham Reference Library)*

Bolts and catches for cupboards and drawers; knockers; eyes for lashings and ropes; handles for coffins, desks and doors; hasps and staples; hinges, hooks, latches, pulleys and sashes were all part of the extensive cabinet brass trade, which is still carried on by Crofts & Assinder. Newman Brothers, in Fleet Street, conducted a specialist part of this trade to make coffin furniture for the funeral business. A fall-off in trade through competition from other sources finally led Newman Brothers to close their doors to business in 1999. Their factory was left untouched and the equipment, which included the old-fashioned fly-press, was allowed to gather dust. During 2003 a scheme was proposed to preserve part of the old factory as a coffin museum.

Naval brass foundry was a speciality chosen by a few manufacturers. Among their ranks were Moore Brothers of Priory Road, Aston and J.E. Cope of Snow Hill. Items included in this range were ships' bells, binnacles, brackets, rings, thimbles and ventilators. Gabriel & Co. and A.B. Row made cabinet, railway and general brass foundry. G. & W. Purser, Trafalgar Works, Palmer Street produced speaking tube fittings.

Those listed above are but a proportion of the many firms which appear in trade directories and other publications. Their products were used as components in many other trades as well as providing fixtures and fittings for the home, transport and the service industries.

MODERN BRASS FOUNDERS AND WORKERS

Despite the continued and increasing use of plastics there is still a regular demand for various types of brass goods for electrical and gas appliances and the plumbing trade. Birmingham brass founders have been considerably depleted in numbers, but a few firms continue to turn out products to suit the needs of the twenty-first century.

The decline of sand casting foundries has been matched by a greater diversity in making and working with brass goods. Armac is one local brass firm that has met the challenges of modern times. The company was formed in 1931 at the Staniforth Street works. Their main business was the making of antique-style brass fittings for the furniture trade, but in recent times they have broadened their range to include kitchen and bathroom products. Another four companies were brought into the fold, two being the Birmingham-based Brass Turned Parts Ltd (formerly of Fallows Road), which specialised in the making of precision turned parts, and Frank Allart & Co. Ltd (of Sherborne Road and later Great Tindal Street), which concentrated on builders' hardware and related products. The other two firms were Dunton & Marston Ltd, who owned a sand casting foundry at Willenhall, and Bentley Brassware Ltd of Walsall, who made brass ornaments. During 2004 Armac transferred their business from Staniforth Street to Dollman Street, in Nechells, where the Bentley Brassware and Brass Turned Parts aspects have also been combined on one site.

Crofts & Assinder were founded during 1875 and were associated with both bedstead manufacture and cabinet brass foundry. This firm was begun as a partnership of George Crofts and George Frederick Assinder and first operated a foundry in Lower Essex Street. The cabinet brasswork trade was moved to the Lombard Street Foundry, when Hoskins & Sewell decided to move their foundry work to Heath Mill Lane. The next move was the separation of the bedstead and cabinet business, when a new company was formed, in 1910, to manage the cabinet trade. Thereafter the two different sides of the business went their separate ways and the bedstead side was eventually absorbed into the Peyton, Hoyland & Barber combine. In modern times the firm has specialised as handle makers, also to work with steel, cast iron, zinc (zamak), ceramics, glass and wood. They also engage in plating and die-casting as part of their varied product range.

Samuel Heath & Sons of Leopold Street have a long history in the trade, and can trace their history back to the founder of their company, Samuel Heath, born in 1813 in Lancaster Street. Samuel's father, John, was associated with the Birmingham gun trade, and was then employed as a gun finisher. Samuel grew up to follow a different occupation, which was the brass trade. He learned the trade of brass founder and was employed in the business when his first son, Thomas, was born in 1834. Trade directories do not record Samuel Heath as having any brass foundry in his own name until 1860, but there was a firm of Heath & Lawton in Great Charles Street and later in Louisa Street, which operated during the 1840s and 1850s, and with which, it seems, Samuel Heath was associated.

Samuel Heath's independent business venture began at 14 Great Charles Street and within a few years had gained enough funds to move to new works at 116 Leopold Street. These premises became his base for the rest of his life and remain the headquarters of the firm today.

Adjacent residential properties were acquired and demolished to make way for improvements to Crofts & Assinder premises. In this view the later extensions can be seen, June 2003. *(Ray Shill)*

CHAPTER FOUR

THE BEDSTEAD TRADE

Metal beds, chairs and couches were generally made from iron or brass or a combination of the two. The making of metallic beds in Birmingham can be traced to Benjamin Cook, brass founders of Caroline Street. By 1812 Benjamin Cook advertised as a jeweller, toy maker and a maker of gas light apparatus. He also traded as the Patent Brass Rod Co. Cook patented, in 1812, a new method of making articles of furniture using rods of metal, or solid iron covered with brass or other metals. He transferred his brass- and iron-founding trade to Whittall Street during the 1820s and by 1831 had relocated again to Bradford Street. Bedsteads seem to have been a long-term product of the firm, but it was not until 1829 that trade directories list B. Cook as a maker of brass and iron bedsteads.

Large-scale metallic bedstead manufacture from brass or iron became a commercial possibility once a satisfactory method of tube making was perfected. For this development the British tube making industry owes a debt of gratitude to an invention of Cornelius Whitehouse in 1824. Whitehouse was then engaged in the edge tool trade and worked for Edward Ewell near Wednesbury. He made two important discoveries. With the first discovery he used the 'hollow fire' that was used widely in the edge tool trade. This method applied heat to a greater area than the blacksmith's hearth and had the potential to assist the making of long lengths of tube. Whitehouse's second fundamental discovery was the process of applying pressure evenly and rapidly to the outside of the tube, forcing the edges of the iron strip against each other until they fused. In this process the end of a heated piece of strip iron was fixed to a winch, called a draw-bench, which quickly pulled the strip through a die, or aperture, causing the edges to come together. Whitehouse was so confident of his invention that he took out a patent in 1825.

Ewell had no need of the tube-making invention, but recommended Whitehouse to the Wednesbury tube maker James Russell. Whitehouse went to work for Russell, who enthusiastically took up the patent. So began the industry of butt-welded tubes that was to give much business to the Wednesbury tube makers.

Wednesbury became noted for the manufacture of gas tubes, but within five years another challenge for the tube maker was presented in the form of the boiler tube. Steam locomotives had multi-tubular boilers. Welded tubes were considered not to have the structural strength to withstand the pressures within the boiler, and tubes with overlapping seams were preferred. The Wednesbury tube makers such as James Russell were never able to capture this market, as they had with the gas tube. Other firms found profits in the locomotive tube trade, which made the tube by cold-drawing metal ingots into tubes of the required diameter. Several were located in Birmingham and the Black Country, contributing to this district's gaining an important reputation for tube making.

Birmingham, and neighbouring Aston, tube makers served a variety of industries that, in addition to the gas and locomotive tube business, supplied the cycle, motorcycle, car and aeroplane industries. Birmingham also had the largest concentration of firms engaged in the metallic bedstead trade in Britain. An important element of the metallic

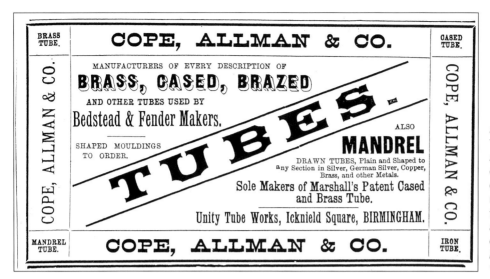

Advertisement for Cased Tubes made by Cope Allman & Co. Ltd. The cased tube industry was essential to bedstead manufacture, where iron tubes were covered with a layer of brass for ornamentation. *(Kelly's Birmingham Directory, 1886)*

bedstead was the tubular parts that formed the basic structure, and a number of local firms made this a speciality. Firms that supplied tubes to the bedstead trade included William Bayliss Ltd, Sheepcote Street; Britannia Tube Co., Glover Street; Cope Allman & Co. Ltd, Icknield Square; and Earle, Bourne & Co. Ltd, Heath Street.

R. Winfield, like Benjamin Cook, was a pioneer in the Birmingham metallic bedstead trade. During 1827 Robert Winfield took out his first bedstead tube patent. Early bedstead construction was hampered by connections coming undone. Those who entered the trade had to find the means of making the connecting parts, which were often made from castings. Winfield devised a new method for assembling brass and iron bedsteads and at the same time laid the foundation of a new industry for Birmingham. The demand for metal bedsteads developed from the relative ease of construction, cleanliness and compact size.

Several other firms would soon join both Cooke and Winfield in the metallic bedstead trade, and bedstead works were distributed throughout Birmingham and the Black Country. Bedsteads were made in all shapes an sizes, ranging from the carefully crafted examples shown at the Great Exhibition of 1851 at Crystal Palace, down to the basic bed supplied for hospital use.

A number of Birmingham bed making firms were established during the 1840s and '50s. Phipson and Warden of Granville Street; Peyton and Harlow of Bordesley; Samuel Whitfield (Gladstone Works); John & Joseph Taunton of Sherborne Road; and G. Marris of Lichfield Street all came into existence during this time.

Iron and brass bedstead makers drew on many skills, including those of the tube maker, blacksmith, varnish maker, wire weaver and brass and iron founder. Many factories were often cramped and cluttered places. Photographs taken in 1902 of the works belonging to Fisher, Brown & Bayley (118–23 Lionel Steet) show workers weaving wire for mattresses, forging bedstead stretchers, cutting rods, fitting brasswork to bedsteads and punching and studding angles for the frame.

Bedstead factories were distributed throughout Birmingham, but the greatest concentration was to be found in the Digbeth and

An artist's impression showing the arrangement of R.W. Winfield's foundry, rolling and bedstead works in Cambridge Street, as seen from Easy Row during the 1850s. Various buildings lined Gibson's private canal basin and canal on all sides. *(Great Western Railway Guide, 1860)*

MESSRS. WINFIELD AND SON'S MANUFACTORY, BIRMINGHAM.

Above: Much of the skill of bedstead making involved metal working in its various forms. Workers are seen at Fisher, Brown & Bayley Bedstead Works, Lionel Street cutting and fitting tubes for the bedstead framework. *(Local Studies Department, Birmingham Reference Library) Below, left:* The smith was essential to the bedstead trade for the shaping and bending of the various components. A smith is seen at his anvil at Fisher, Brown & Bayley Bedstead Works. *(Local Studies Department, Birmingham Reference Library) Below, right:* Mattress making was done chiefly by female workers, who were employed to weave wire into a patterned mesh for the mattress. In this view workers are seen at mattress machines at Fisher, Brown & Bayley Bedstead Works. *(Local Studies Department, Birmingham Reference Library)*

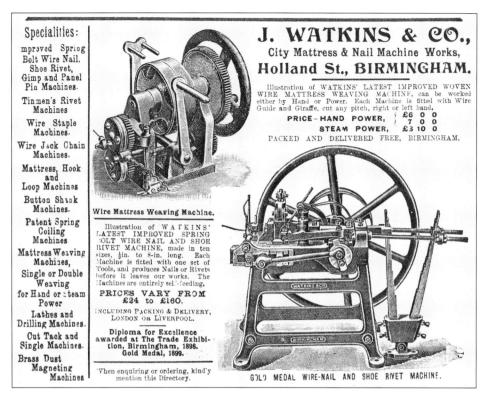

Deritend district of the town. Samuel Whitfield founded a bedstead and safe manufactory in 1849 that was first carried on at 38 Oxford Street and later acquired additional premises across the road at no. 52. Samuel's son, Samuel Benjamin Whitfield, joined the firm in 1857, and other sons also became associated in company affairs once they were of age. Their bedstead factory was transferred to the Gladstone Works, Watery Lane, during 1866, where they occupied a large site located between nos 109 and 125. The assets of Samuel Whitfield & Sons were split four ways from 1871, when Frederic Whitfield took charge of the fireproof safe trade, James Whitfield controlled the brass foundry business and Samuel Whitfield Snr carried on the bedding trade. Samuel Benjamin Whitfield had the management of the bedstead factory.

Bedstead making at the Watery Lane factory was described in the April 1875 edition of the *Furniture Gazette*. Welded iron tubes were delivered to the cutting rooms in straight lengths to be cut up and shaped into the forms required. Some of the cut sections were then fitted with studs, on which the laths were mounted when the bed was made up. Iron rods, once cut to size and studded, were taken to the 'bending' gallery above the casting shop, where they were bent and shaped in vices to a required design.

These pieces of metal, which formed the components of the head and foot of the bed, were then taken down to the ground floor casting shop. The casting shop contained the cupolas where pig iron was melted. Each length of tube, bent or otherwise, was laid out on a frame. Tube endings were placed in 'chills', 'stocks' or moulds, which formed a linked pattern that made up the shape of the head or foot. Molten iron was poured into each chill, and after a period of time the chills were opened to reveal an ornamental cast shape. These linking shapes were then trimmed and cleaned. Similar castings made on the corners of the posts made the sockets into which dovetail joints and ends of angle iron were fitted. Adjoining the foundry was the stock room, where the different chills, or stocks, were kept. The many and varied patterns required for bed design led to a large number of stocks being held in store.

Iron was prone to rusting and required a protective coating. Bedstead components were taken to the japanning and painting department. The work was carried out in different shops, and it was in this department that the many types of decoration were performed. The common, or black, japanning was done on the ground floor. Bedsteads from the casting shop were covered with a coating of black japan and placed in large stoves, or heated rooms. On other floors green or maroon japan work was done. In fact, different qualities of finishes were produced according to public demand, and better quality work also commanded a higher retail price.

Brass bedsteads were also considered as part of the higher quality range of bedsteads. The frameworks of these beds were usually of iron, while the pillars and rails tubes were brass cased. Castings of brass were also fitted to the framework. All brass work was covered with layers of lacquer.

S.B. Whitfield carried on the bedstead factory until his death in 1885. He was also associated with a steel pen factory, the Lion Works, in Broad Street. Samuel Benjamin Whitfield commenced making steel pens during the year 1878 and was probably encouraged to enter this business by the profits made by existing pen firms, such as Gillot's. For Whitfield this proved to be an expensive venture and the pen trade came close to ruining him. An official receiver was appointed in February 1884, but fortunately creditors agreed to accept part payment of their debts rather than forcing Whitfield into bankruptcy.

The pen business was sold off after S.B. Whitfield's estate had been settled, but bedstead manufacture was continued for several years at the Watery Lane Works as S.B. Whifield & Co. Samuel Whitfield the father outlived Samuel the son by some seven years. After Samuel Whitfield Snr died the complex working arrangements that included the Oxford Street and Watery Lane establishments were eventually reconciled as two limited companies. The Whitfield's Bedstead Co. Ltd took charge of the bedstead factory, while the other company ran the safe factory.

S. B. WHITFIELD,
MANUFACTURER OF
METALLIC BEDSTEADS, COTS, CHAIRS, &c.,
GLADSTONE WORKS,
WATERY LANE, BIRMINGHAM.

The Gladstone Works were located between Watery Lane & New Bond Street. These premises became the bedstead factory of S.B. Whitfield & Co. *(Kelly's Directory, 1875)*

Edward Hatton started a separate bedstead and safe works at 62 Oxford Street in about 1851, and by 1854 was trading as a partnership of Taunton, Hatton & Johnson. A new factory was built on a strip of land next to Atkin & Son's, Sheffield Works, in Rea Street South, where saws and planes were made. Edwin Atkin engaged a builder, J. Griffith, to erect the factory, and arrangements were made with John Richard Cromwell Taunton and Joseph Taunton for the lease once the buildings were completed. The terms of the lease were based on a yearly rental of £50 plus increments of £7 10s for every £100 'laid out and expended' by Edward Atkin in providing the necessary accommodation. Griffith's contract price was £495, but with extras came to nearly £549, but a rent of £91 6s 6d was finally agreed. Taunton & Hatton's bedstead works were transferred from Oxford Street to the Rea Street South factory during 1857, where the new works became known as the Vaughton Works. By 1870 Taunton Brothers had moved their business again. They relocated this time to a new, and larger, factory known as the Belgrave Works, which was built in Sherbourne Road, Balsall Heath. John & Joseph Taunton made metallic and wooden beds, hospital beds and safes there.

A leading member of the Taunton firm was Joseph Taunton. Joseph was born in Bristol in 1833, and was educated at King Edward's School in Birmingham. He was also a director of Palmer Tyre Co. and represented Solihull on Warwickshire Council. Joseph retired in 1895 and died in 1921.

Taunton's bedstead business remained at the Belgrave Works until about 1936. By this time they had commenced a new trade in gas meter production. The Taunton family were also associated with the firm of Taunton, Selkirk & Co. Ltd, which made mattresses in River Street, Balsall Heath. Declining bedstead sales led both firms to relocate to new premises in Eyre Street, near to another bedstead maker, Albert Philips Ltd. J. & J. Taunton then came to concentrate production on the gas meter trade.

Peyton & Harlow established a factory at High Street, Bordesley and became one of Birmingham's most successful firms. Their business was formed during 1843, when land was acquired at 96 High Street for the first part of the works. The management of the business was left in the hands of Jonathan Harlow, who had already gained experience in the trade at Holloway Head. Metallic bedstead manufacturers were keen to devise simple systems for linking sections of the bed together and any new system devised could benefit sales. Dovetail jointing had been available for metallic bedstead assembly following the patent granted to John Bennett in 1813. In December 1841 Jonathan Harlow and William Church patented an improved method of joining tubes together that was to prove the foundation of Harlow's bedstead business.

Dr William Church was a man of restless enterprise and had been involved with several engineering and commercial projects, which included the London & Birmingham Steam Carriage Co. Church lived in High Street, in a house adjacent to the new bedstead factory, but his skill lay with producing new ideas and he lacked the finances for development. It would seem that Richard Peyton provided the money for this bedstead venture and it was his name that appears on the initial leases.

Peyton had other business commitments, and when the first partnership papers were drawn up on 1 January 1850 clauses ensured that Harlow would give his total time to

Peyton & Harlow's metallic bedstead works, High Street, Bordesley. *(Cornish's Guide of Birmingham, 1853)*

the bedstead company, while Peyton would deal with the accounts but was free to devote his time elsewhere. A year later a relative, Edward Peyton, was admitted to the partnership and from 1851 the bedstead makers were known as Peyton, Harlow & Peyton.

Birmingham's successful bed making firms all had patents that protected both their methods of manufacture and their designs. An essential part of Peyton & Harlow's bed was the dovetail joint. It was a design that was free from screws, bolts or nuts and even dispensed with tools for assembly or taking down. It was a design that was perfected, to some extent, in the patent of 1847 that bears the names of Richard Peyton, Jonathan Harlow and Thomas Horne. The essential components of any metallic bed structure were the laths and rails. With the Peyton, Harlow and Horne design a stud and slot system was used as a means of fastening the laths and rails together.

An extensive bedstead factory was built up between 1844 and 1853 through acquisition of adjacent property, which was bounded by High Street, Warner Street and Warwick Street. Harlow died in November 1854 and management of the business passed to Edward Peyton. The firm then traded as Peyton & Peyton.

Edward Peyton was the second son of Abel Peyton, manufacturing chemist, of Oxygen Street. Younger brother Henry assisted Edward Peyton at the Bordesley Bedstead Works and together the brothers came to build on the trade established by Harlow. Many aspects of bedstead making were carried out on the High Street site. An inventory of the plant made in 1884 illustrates the different departments there, which included tube making, casting shops, smith shops and lacquer departments.

1884 inventory of Peyton & Peyton (*As detailed in MS 119, Birmingham Archives*)

Carpenters shops, paint cellars, lacquering room, smithies, rail fitting galleries, brass bed finishing, iron and sand casting shop, core making shop, sand brass casting shop, cot fitting gallery, case fitting shop, brass department with tube cutting machines, angle iron casting shop, piercing angle department, brass strip casting shop, tube department, mattress department, sacking department, turned brass department and a rough warehouse.

Edward Peyton died 1906, aged about seventy-eight. He had been involved with the metallic bedstead trade for fifty-five years.

Some 100,000 bedsteads were produced each year by Peyton & Peyton Ltd at their Bordesley Works. Three basic stages were involved in production. The first stage was design and modelling, the second was the foundry stage where different parts were cast, and the third was japanning and coating with white enamel.

Many bedstead workers belonged to the Bedstead Workers Association, which was a union dedicated to improving working conditions and pay. Local bedstead makers were affected by industrial action during the winter of 1908 and 1909, when union members went on strike. The strike was organised and led by G. Jones, president of the Association. By January 1909 their action was far from a resolution. About 1,200 men assembled in Ryder Street. The strikers marched by way of Corporation Street, New Street, Broad Street and Sheepcote Street to Philips & Son, brass and iron bedstead makers and fire-proof safe manufacturers. They then returned by way of Broad Street and Bolton Street to pass the works of Hoskins & Sewell, Peyton & Son, and then Whitfield & Co. in Watery Lane.

The union believed they had the whip-hand as their members were the 'cream of the trade' and the masters would not be able to carry on without them. Some may have been veterans of the 1889 strike that came close to crippling the industry but ended amicably

Extract of Schedule of Fixed Plant, Peyton & Peyton *(PROBT31/32228/45098)*

PACKING ROOM AND WAREHOUSE, fronting to High Street Bordesley: Two large hand lifts serving first floor each with cage 5 feet 6 inches by 6 feet inside; safety gates and hoisting gear; the system of about 165 yards of 24 inch gauge tram lines as laid in warehouse with 5 turntables and weighbridge.

MESS ROOM, 2nd Floor: Lavatory basin and fittings

ORNAMENTING AND FITTING-UP SHOP. No.6, 1st Floor: High-pressure hot water boiler in connection with lacquering stoves in shop overhead.

BRASS FITTING SHOP, No.5, 2nd Floor: Ventilating Fan.

LACQUERING SHOP, 2nd Floor: Iron-topped brick-built fire-heated lacquering stove, 10 feet by 3 feet 6 inches with flue pipe. Iron water-piping with brass valve and cap. Brick-built lacquering stove 5 feet by 8 feet 6 inches by 7 feet 6 inches with rolling racks and 10 feet extension fitted with four rolling trays, heated by special high pressure apparatus and hydraulic piping fitted. Gas-heated lacquering stove with riveted iron case, 7 feet by 3 feet 6 inches inside partly covered with brick-work and fitted with three rolling racks.

STOVES: Central block of 19 blacking stoves in 3 stories heated by high pressure hot water coils, having special heater in basement, complete with all gauges, iron doors and other fittings.

ENAMELLING SHOPS, ground and 1st Floor: Steam trap. Belt-driven ventilating fan with countershafts and belting to drive same and deal casings to belts.

ENGINE ROOM; Wood partition enclosing engine room. 16 hp Tangye Horizontal steam engine with turned flywheel, Porter governor, steam and exhaust piping and all fittings on and brick foundation.

SMITH SHOP: Underground line of about 10 ft of 3½ inch main shafting in iron-covered brick-lined race with main spur wheel, all necessary bearings and couplings and driving pulleys to the various machines including 1 pulley 6 feet diameter; 20 h.p Tangye steam engine with porter governor, lubricator fly wheel, main spur wheel and all fittings and piping on brick foundations; line of about 40ft of 2¾ in turned shafting with 7 plummer blocks, 3 couplings, 9 iron pulleys ranging 4 ft to 1 ft diameter; 2 brick-built double hearths each with fittings and blast services; 2 single ditto; 1 small heating furnace; small steam pump with piping and steam trap (near 20 hp engine); blast service pipe to cupola and hearths; steam trap; ditto; the cast iron floor plates covering shaft races and certain other small portions of smith's shop floor.

POLISHING AND PLATING SHOP: Lead floor tray near acid vats, worn.

ART METAL ROOM: Deal partition across room with nest of stock shelves attached.

ART METAL DEPARTMENT, Department Offices: Matchboard partition enclosing lavatory with lavatory basin and W.C. fittings.

CASTING SHOP: Two wooden moulding tubs; 2 pot furnaces with chimney and ash pit.

TIME OFFICE AND GATEWAY: Wagon-weighing machine to weigh 8 tons.

OUTSIDE: Fifty wire window guards to Warwick Street and Warner Street frontages.

BOILER HOUSE: Babcock & Willcox tubular steam boiler about 90 hp in brickwork 6 ft 6 in by 20 ft. complete with all valves, fittings and connections, set to blow at 100 lbs pressure.

PRINTING ROOM: Three-inch wrought iron heating piping as fitted in printing and pattern rooms, total about 90 ft with valve.

GALLERY ROUND FOUNDRY: Large ventilating fan fixed in gable of building.

ENGINE ROOM: 12 hp horizontal steam engine with governor, lubricator, turned fly wheel main pulley and all fittings and piping and extended main shaft with 4 ft pulley; four-pole lighting dynamo for 110 volts 55 amp at 950 r.p.m. on slide rails with deal guard (by the Lister Co., Dursley); 6 in driving belt to ditto; main switch board 30 in by 26 in with voltmeter switches and cables to the various departments; 3 in second motion shaft in 2 bearings with 4 pulleys and stone foundations; 5 ft intermediate wheel on 4in shaft with 2 bearings; line of about 110 feet of 2 in and 2 in shafting extending through the foundry with 11 bearings, 13 pulleys and driving belt; 24 feet of 3 in shafting with spur pinion, 3 iron pulleys, 2 wall boxes and special brackets; 13 iron floor plates.

PAINT STORES; Four-inch heating piping as fixed with gas heater.

SACKING SHOP: Iron floor grids, iron door and frame and hanging racks in stove; corner lavatory with water tap and waste pipe.

Also METER SHOP, STOCK ROMS, GENERAL OFFICES and other LAVATORIES etc., as set forth in Messr Edwards, Son & Bigwood's Schedule, 31 March 1916.

The former Peyton & Peyton factory was sold to Fisher & Ludlow, which converted the factory for the needs of their business, which then centred on the automobile trade. Part of the factory was demolished and rebuilt, but some of the original buildings were retained. In this general view of Bordesley High Street, looking towards Birmingham, the Fisher & Ludlow Material Handling department is clearly marked. Next door to these premises is part of Peyton & Peyton's former bedstead works, while further along the street on the same side are the range of buildings that was the Hoskins & Sewell Bedstead Works. *(Local Studies Department, Birmingham Reference Library)*

through the careful arbitration of the Mayor, Councillor Clayton. This time the bedstead makers were more determined and recruited new staff. Questioned on this point, a member of the firm of Taunton & Co. said that the expense in engaging new staff to take the place of union men who had gone had proved the old adage 'there are as many good fish in the sea as ever come out'. Even though parts the Taunton works were not at full strength, a number of the old men came back and production was not seriously affected. A number of strikers stayed out for another month, but the strike had clearly been broken. By February, bedstead firms such as Hoskins & Sewell were receiving applications from bedstead workers for vacant positions.

A feature of the bedstead trade was the establishment of a London office and agencies in different parts of the world to sell its products. Peyton had a bedstead works and office in Paris (established in about 1894) to cope with the French trading laws as well as agencies in the Middle East, Australia and Asia.

Competition between bedstead makers was heightened after 1900, with both local and foreign metallic and wooden bedstead makers. Peyton & Peyton merged with John Hoyland (Western Road), Barber & Son (West Bromwich) and Crofts & Assinder (Heath Mill Lane) to form Peyton, Hoyland & Barber in October 1916.

Another three local bedstead firms joined this partnership later. They were Philips & Son, Sheepcote Street (1918), J Troman (1918) and the Birmingham Metallic Bedstead Co. (mattress makers) in 1919. It was a significant merger that concentrated production at the Peyton & Peyton company factory. Hoyland's works, and those of Crofts & Assinder, Philips & Son and Troman were closed down and the buildings disposed of.

Ebenezer Hoskins, the son of a Plymouth gun lock filer, started the firm of Hoskins & Sewell. Hoskins was born in Exeter, in 1824, but came with his family to the West Midlands and was indentured as an apprentice coachsmith with Matthew Hawkins of Wednesbury in 1839. He later moved to Aston and by 1851 was working as a smith and living at Walnut Terrace, Deritend, with his young wife, Charlotte, son Frederick and daughter Mary. John Key, blacksmith, lived nearby at 20 Court, High Street, Bordesley. Hoskins and Key decided to go into partnership in about 1854, and initially made beds at 151 High Street, Bordesley before moving to larger premises at 77–83 High Street. John Key lived at the works, while Hoskins moved to Highgate.

Business improved and both Hoskins and Key prospered. They belonged to a select band of bedstead makers, which included Peyton, Taunton and Whitfield, that had offices in London and were able to tap into the lucrative export market.

Key & Hoskins' London representative, E.H. Sewell, later joined the partnership and for a brief time this firm traded as Key, Hoskins & Sewell. John Key then left the firm to set up a separate bedstead business. By 1875 Key had offices and show rooms at the Commercial Buildings, Dudley Street. Beds appear to have been constructed at 39 Dudley Street and Key also traded as a varnish maker at 135 Glover Street. Key's business proved not to be a success and by 1878 he had formed another partnership, with furniture dealer John Teychenne, to make bedding at Glover Street. This business also failed and John Key ceased to trade as a bedstead maker.

Meanwhile the fortunes of the Hoskins & Sewell company continued to improve. In about 1866 Key & Hoskins had acquired the iron and brass cased tube works of Ferdinand Potts & Co. that occupied a strip of land between Charles Henry Street and Lombard Street. Part became the Lombard Street Foundry, and the Charles Henry Street side was retained as a tube works. The tube works was constructed on land reclaimed from the bed of the old course of the River Rea. Access to the works was gained either from Lombard Street or through a passageway between nos 23 and 24 Charles Henry Street. The tube business was later moved to larger premises bounded by Floodgate Street and Heath Mill Lane and the building at Charles Henry Street was sub-let. They also acquired a depot at Hoxton in London, which assisted their foreign trade.

Ebenezer Hoskins died in 1892, leaving sons Frederick and John to look after the family interests in the firm. These were changing times and competition in the bedstead trade, in Britain and abroad, was becoming intense. Agencies were distributed through Europe, Africa and Australia. Hoskins & Sewell even had a representative in America. Following the lead of another local bedstead maker, Peyton & Peyton, members of the Hoskins firm decided to register as a limited company.

Hoskins & Sewell Ltd was formed in May 1897. The first meeting of Hoskins & Sewell was held at the High Street offices, Bordesley in June 1897. Frederick Hoskins, John Ebenezer Hoskins, Edward Henry Sewell and Edward Leppingwell Sewell were the principal shareholders. Their business was carried on in Birmingham at a number of sites. Bedsteads were assembled at the main works in High Street. Tubes continued to be made

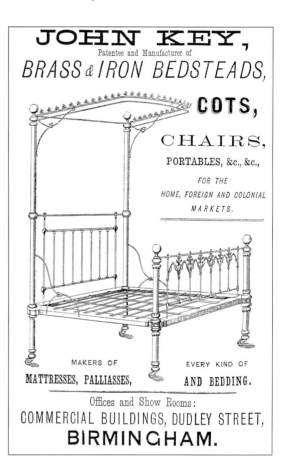

John Key was first in partnership with Hoskins at the Midland Bedstead Works, before briefly setting up as independent bedstead maker. *(Kelly's Directory of Birmingham, 1875)*

Hoskins & Sewell invoice, 1897, showing the main factory at Bordesley as well as a bedding factory in London and a warehouse in New York. (Edwards Brothers MSS)

at the rolling mills located between Floodgate Street and Heath Mill Lane, and brass castings were produced at Lombard Street foundry. Bedding was made in London at their Eagle Wharf Road premises in Hoxton. Hoskins & Sewell also leased stables at Warwick Wharf, Fazeley Street and sent a significant quantity of bedstead parts by Fellows, Morton & Clayton boats to Eagle Wharf, London.

It was decided in July 1898 to give up the Lombard Street foundry and purchase the brass founding business of Oldham & Bower in Heath Mill Lane, which lay close to the tube works. The Lombard Street works were retained for another two years and were eventually sold during 1900. The buyer of this foundry was Crofts & Assinder, who continue to make cabinet brassware on this site.

Frederick Hoskins died in 1898 and William Parish Hoskins took his place as a company director. During April 1900 arrangements were made to purchase Hoskins Brothers Mattress Works at Hay Mills from W.P. Hoskins, who at the time was the sole proprietor. Hoskins & Sewell Ltd was reconstructed during 1900, when Hoskins & Sewell (1900) Ltd was formed. The new company share issue provided much-needed capital for expansion, and particularly for new buildings at Hay Mills.

Bedstead making remained highly competitive and total commitment was required from the managers. During 1902 the matter of Charles Harvey came before the Board. Harvey was a talented inventor with a string of patents to his name and to that of the company, among them improvements to cased tubing and a new method called paper tubes (1901). Despite his inventive ability, his post as manager of the tube works was up for review during a works reorganisation. Charles Harvey resigned, and Mr R. Winterton took his place. The tube mills then comprised an iron shop, cased tube mill, paper tube mill, polishing shop, a mount shop and lacquering department.

Patent rights were particularly complicated in the bedstead trade, as it encompassed so many manufacturing disciplines. Patents pertaining to parts for bedsteads, cots and berths, mattresses, tube manufacture, and improved means of painting and lacquering all came into the equation. The leading Birmingham bedstead manufacturers had a whole portfolio of patents which supported their bed making. The close similarities of some patents frequently led to legal action when one company sought compensation from another. In such situations the only real winners were the barristers and solicitors who found lucrative work in the legal minefield of the hundreds and thousands of patent records and laws.

All aspects of the business at Hoskins & Sewell were under constant review, but particular attention was given to the working of the tube and brass foundry departments. The managers of these respective departments had to ensure that each was profitable. New markets were also sought and a new development instituted at this time was the making of ships' berths in a part of the shop at the High Street Works.

A separate brass foundry location proved to be an expensive luxury in a city full of brass foundries, and despite the additional revenue received from cabinet brass foundry

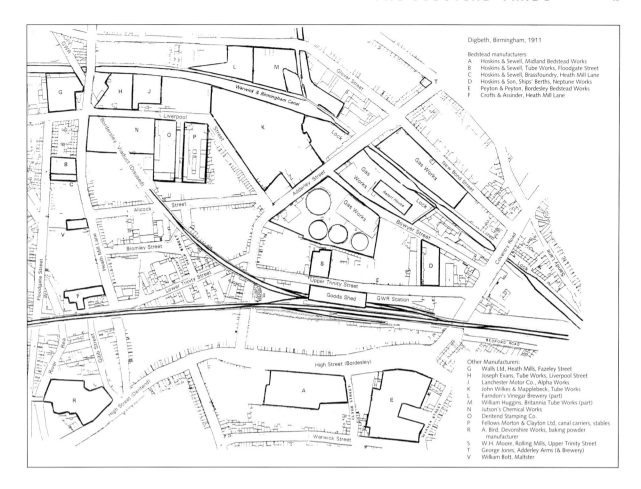

Digbeth, Birmingham, 1911

Bedstead manufacturers:
A   Hoskins & Sewell, Midland Bedstead Works
B   Hoskins & Sewell, Tube Works, Floodgate Street
C   Hoskins & Sewell, Brassfoundry, Heath Mill Lane
D   Hoskins & Son, Ships' Berths, Neptune Works
E   Peyton & Peyton, Bordesley Bedstead Works
F   Crofts & Assinder, Heath Mill Lane

Other Manufacturers:
G   Walls Ltd, Heath Mills, Fazeley Street
H   Joseph Evans, Tube Works, Liverpool Street
J   Lanchester Motor Co., Alpha Works
K   John Wilkes & Mapplebeck, Tube Works
L   Farndon's Vinegar Brewery (part)
M   William Huggins, Britannia Tube Works (part)
N   Jutson's Chemical Works
O   Deritend Stamping Co.
P   Fellows Morton & Clayton Ltd, canal carriers, stables
R   A. Bird, Devonshire Works, baking powder
        manufacturer
S   W.H. Moore, Rolling Mills, Upper Trinity Street
T   George Jones, Adderley Arms (& Brewery)
V   William Bott, Maltster

A map of Digbeth showing the main bedstead works, 1911.

work, closure became inevitable. The Heath Mill Street foundry was closed down during 1909, and all obsolete castings were melted down. The old buildings were eventually vacated at the end of 1912 and leased for other use. Hoskins & Sewell meanwhile were keen to keep with the latest methods and cost-saving devices. During 1913 they adopted a new process for painting and enamelling bedsteads, using patent special finishes made by George Cadby & Sons.

In 1913 the metallic bedstead trade was one of the least successful of Birmingham's industries. At no time during that year did demand approach production capacity, and in consequence workers were put on short time or their services were dispensed with. There had been a continued reduction in demand for metal beds, and wooden bedsteads had become more fashionable than they had ever been. Matters were not been helped by the Metallic Bedstead Manufacturers Federation, which had been formed in 1912. They represented most Birmingham bedstead manufacturers, but had instituted a rebate scheme that had alienated the retail trade, leading many retailers to promote the wooden rather than the metallic products.

Hoskins & Sewell decided to enter the wooden bedstead trade, and during January 1914 made alterations to the Hay Mills works to install wood-cutting machines. Production also changed to suit the war effort, and included tubes for aircraft construction, in particular the supply of tubes to the Standard Aircraft Co.

The market for metallic bedsteads continued to decline after the war, and the company disposed of some of its assets. First to be sold was the Heath Mill Street brass foundry, in 1920, to Fosters Accessories, who sub-let the building to the Birmingham Tyre & Valve Co. Further changes happened in 1925, when company involvement with Eagle Wharf Road premises ceased on the sale of the lease to R. Legge & Co.

A new line of business, the making of steel window frames, was commenced at Bordesley Street. The metal window department was soon increased in size and moved to the Clyde Street side of the property. These were difficult years for the metallic bedstead trade. Firms were forced to make economies and several left the trade altogether. Hoskins & Sewell closed their tube rolling mills in 1932 and transferred the tube factory offices and warehouse to Bordesley.

Peyton, Hoyland & Barber's business was also in decline. In 1931 arrangements were made with Hoskins & Sewell to supply their metallic bed orders. The agreement lasted for about eighteen months, before Peytons decided to cease trading completely. During 1933 Hoskins & Sewell agreed to take over of the business of Peyton, Hoyland & Barber, which had gone into receivership. A new company, Peyton, Hoyland & Barber (1933) Ltd, was formed to manage their remaining metallic bedstead trade. Hoskins & Sewell held most of the share capital. The old Peyton factory retained a mattress department at 71–83 High Street that was under the management of Fred Biggins. This mattress factory was closed down in 1934 and the work transferred to Hay Mills. The extensive factory at High Street, Bordesley, occupied by Peyton, Hoyland & Barber, was sold to Fisher & Ludlow, who demolished most of the buildings and replaced them with a new factory that supplied pressed parts to the motor car industry.

Metallic bedstead manufacture in the city continued to decline. Hoskins & Sewell's finances were, however, better than most, as their business was buoyed up through sales of the wooden bedsteads made at Hay Mills and the metal window trade. Government contracts also provided much-needed revenue during the Second World War. Hoskins & Sewell made Bailey Bridges and geared up with new plant for the bridge work in 1942 and 1943, including a heavy press, drills, and angle-bending machines.

By 1950 the numbers of local bedstead makers had dwindled to a few principal firms, which included Hoskins & Sewell, A. Phillips, Whitfield's Bedsteads, Slumberland & Wales from Birmingham, and Evered in Smethwick and Vono at Tipton. Whitfield's bedstead business was taken over by Hoskins & Sewell in August 1958 and a new company, S.B. Whitfield (Sales) Ltd, was formed to manage the making of hospital beds, hospital equipment and ships' berths at the Watery Lane factory. The rights for manufacture of Volvex Castors were given over to British Castors Ltd in a separate agreement.

Whitfield's best-known product was the Lawson Tait range of hospital beds, which was devised by Lawson Tait in 1881. Lawson was a doctor and surgeon who had a private hospital at the Crescent, Cambridge Street. He had been concerned about the standard of beds then existing, and set about preparing a specification for a new design that suited the needs of the patient. His bed was generally larger (6ft 3in long and 3ft wide), with rounded headers and footers

S.B. Whitfield workers and a Lawson Tait bedstead. Dr Lawson Tait devised a sturdy bed for hospital use. George Gale of Upper Dean Street provided the mattress and S.B. Whitfield assembled the frame. In this photograph five Whitfield workers are standing on the bed to show the strength of the design. *(Hoskins & Sewell MS, Archives Department, Birmingham Reference Library)*

formed in tubular metal. S.B. Whitfield was given the task of construcing the beds, while George Gale, Upper Dean Street, provided the mattresses. The Lawson Tait design proved to be a success, and the good doctor allowed his name to be given to a range of beds produced by Whitfield.

Hoskins & Sewell remained at Bordesley until 1963, when the Midland Works were vacated. Hoskins & Sewell had acquired a disused stamping works in Charlotte Road, Stirchley, and made the necessary building alterations to convert the premises into a bedstead factory and the Charlotte Road premises became the new Midland Works.

Attempts to dispose of the old Midland Works proved difficult, as Birmingham Public Works department was unwilling to grant orders for alternative use for the site. Interested parties included petrol station owners and building construction firms, but the delay in concluding a sale was a burden on company finances in what was proving to be yet another very difficult period in the bedstead trade.

By 1963 Hoskins & Sewell had absorbed the S.B. Whitfield bedstead business into their company and, in the process, had gained many orders from the hospital bed and ships' berth trade, which Whitfield had come to specialise in. The wood-working department at Hay Mills also continued to flourish, and usually turned in a profit for the firm. Additional premises in nearby Charles Street assisted production at Hay Mills and often dealt with specialist orders and new design work. Also in 1963, the firm lost two key members through retirement, H.R. Hoskins and H.V. Robbins. H.R. Hoskins decided to leave the firm once the move to Charlotte Road was complete. He had joined the firm in 1908, had held the post of director for thirty-nine years and had been chairman of the company and managing director for twenty-nine years.

Metallic bed making at Charlotte Street was often worked at a loss, despite new orders being won. Sales managers made trips to Africa and Europe to gain new business. This

Hoskins & Sewell factory and Bordesley Flyover. The old Peyton & Peyton premises had been demolished by the time the Bordesley Flyover was constructed. The Hoskins & Sewell bedstead factory remained and can be seen on the right. *(Local Studies Department, Birmingham Reference Library)*

was the time of the Common Market and emerging African nations, and, with the loss of traditional customers from the old British Empire, the company was keen to tap into new markets. One potential area for new business was hospital beds and furniture. Investment in the National Health Service had led to a programme of purchasing new beds and equipment. Hoskins & Sewell soon became a leading supplier in this field. A valuable addition to this trade was the business of J.A. Smith (London) Ltd, a maker of stainless steel hospital equipment, which was acquired during 1964.

Various factors now contrived to handicap the independent existence of Hoskins & Sewell. They were long-term survivors in a trade where intense competition had prevailed from the start of the twentieth century. Every problem had seemingly been dealt with, but now several new problems presented themselves. On 16 December 1964 a serious fire destroyed a section of the Hay Mill works and handicapped production there for some twelve months. Business from Hay Mills had been carrying the company forward despite the continued losses at Stirchley. Even though some manufacturing was transferred to Charles Street, production was down and sales were affected. The inability to sell off the old Bordesley factory also continued to be a financial burden and the inflexible policies of Birmingham Corporation must share some of the blame in this issue. Permission was eventually given for alternative use of the Bordesley site, but not before demolition of some of the buildings had commenced.

During December 1966 enquiries for sale of the company were made to Evereds, Slumberland and Hoskins & Horton Ltd. It was Hoskins & Horton Ltd, who then owned Hoskins Ltd, of the Neptune Works, Upper Trinity Street, who decided to enter into negotiations for the purchase of Hoskins & Sewell. The arrangement was sealed and ratified in March 1967.

Hoskins & Son had founded the Neptune Works in Upper Trinity Street to make ships' berths. William Parish Hopkins had been the founder, but had relinquished control when Hoskins & Sons Ltd was formed in 1897. Chairman of the new company was Neville Chamberlain, and he took an active role in the management of the firm before pursuing his parliamentary career.

William Parish Hoskins was another son of Ebenezer Hoskins. He worked for Hoskins & Sewell for a time, but then chose to live abroad for a number of years, before returning in the late 1880s to establish the Trinity Street ships' berth factory. William evidently belonged to that restless group of inventors that did so much to further local industry. His numerous patents led to metallic berths being adopted by most ship owners. He died young, aged only 56, after collapsing in a first-class railway carriage when returning to Birmingham during August 1904.

Hoskins & Son's Neptune Works in Upper Trinity Street. *(Heartland Press Collection)*

The supply of metallic bedsteads and berths for ships was a specialist trade. Hoskins became one of three Birmingham manufacturers that catered for this market, the other two being the previously mentioned Hoskins & Sewell and, to a lesser extent, Whitfield. Hoskins did well from this market and supplied bedsteads for many new ocean liners that became part of the fleets for White Star and Cunard. Hoskins' berths were particularly suited for the crew and immigrants' quarters that were an essential part of every ship's accommodation.

Immigration to Canada from northern Europe and to South America from southern Europe encouraged a boom in the ship building trade from 1905. Hoskins received orders for berths to fit a number of new vessels, which included the Cunard 'fliers' *Lusitania* and *Mauretania* and the White Star Line's *Adriatic*. Berths were also supplied for troop ships, and in 1907 berths were required for ships repatriating Prussian troops after the war with Manchuria.

The manufacture of portable wooden bulkheads was commenced during 1907, and it was decided to erect a joinery shop at Trinity Street to make them. Another development was the company involvement with galvanising and tinning. Hoskins had considered the idea of starting their own galvanising plant, but decided against the scheme once the true nature of the work was investigated. They chose instead to take an interest in an existing galvanising works and during 1908 signed an agreement with Walls Ltd, Crown Galvanising Works, Fazeley Street. Neville Chamberlain took a seat on the board of Walls Ltd during September 1908.

The Hoskins & Son works in Trinity Street were enlarged from time to time as adjacent properties were acquired in Trinity Street and Bowyer Street. Plant was also improved and modernised as finances allowed. A new foundry cupola was supplied during 1912 by the Thames Ironworks, that was fitted with a blower from the local engineering firm of Alldays & Onions. Other work included a new lacquering store, as well as extensions to the wood shop made during 1913 and the cabinet shop in 1914.

Important orders were received from the War Office in 1914 that included a large contract to supply ambulance berths for railway carriages, together with mattresses, bolsters, ships' berths and fittings. The Admiralty Transport Department also ordered swinging cots, a special design by the firm, and beds for use on hospital ships.

Hoskins & Son's Minute Book No. 2 1916–43 Summary of quantity supplied (March 1916)		
	Cots	Stanchions
Transport Department to July 1915	5,539	8,316
Transport Department (since start of war)	7,293	11,026
For Transport Vessels 1915	5,109 two-tier berths	
English and Continental Ambulance Trains		
Sleeping Berths supplied 1915	3,590	
Sleeping Berths supplied since start of war	5,934	
Total of Mark II berths to War Office Since start of War	15,600	

Further orders followed for folding bedsteads, ambulance train berths and cabinet work for HM Office of Works.

Company profits showed a marked decline after hostilities ceased. Careful investment in stocks and shares was to provide a useful buffer when finances dwindled. The decline in supply of ships' berths was somewhat counteracted by the supply of hospital beds, metal work from the sheet iron department and carpentry such as cabinets from the wood working section.

Hoskins lost the dedicated services of Neville Chamberlain from 1919 after his election to Parliament. Neville continued to sign meeting minutes until 1935, when he resigned from his position of director and chairman of the company.

During 1936 Hoskins, Hoskins & Sewell and Whitfield's Bedsteads formed themselves into an association for the making of ships' berths and made agreements with

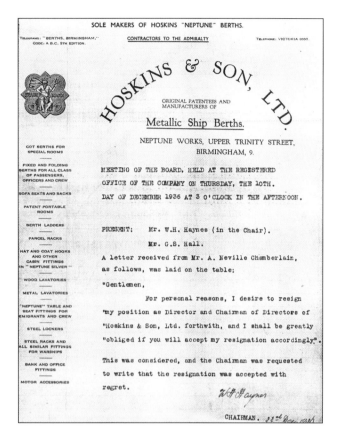

SOLE MAKERS OF HOSKINS "NEPTUNE" BERTHS.

TELEGRAMS: "BERTHS, BIRMINGHAM."   CONTRACTORS TO THE ADMIRALTY   TELEPHONE: VICTORIA 0052.
CODE: A.B.C. 5TH EDITION.

HOSKINS & SON, LTD.

ORIGINAL PATENTEES AND
MANUFACTURERS OF

Metallic Ship Berths.

NEPTUNE WORKS, UPPER TRINITY STREET,
BIRMINGHAM, 9.

COT BERTHS FOR
SPECIAL ROOMS

FIXED AND FOLDING
BERTHS FOR ALL CLASS
OF PASSENGERS,
OFFICERS AND CREW

SOFA SEATS AND BACKS

PATENT PORTABLE
ROOMS

BERTH LADDERS

PARCEL RACKS

HAT AND COAT HOOKS
AND OTHER
CABIN FITTINGS
IN "NEPTUNE SILVER"

WOOD LAVATORIES

METAL LAVATORIES

"NEPTUNE" TABLE AND
SEAT FITTINGS FOR
EMIGRANTS AND CREW

STEEL LOCKERS

STEEL RACKS AND
ALL SIMILAR FITTINGS
FOR WARSHIPS

BANK AND OFFICE
FITTINGS

MOTOR ACCESSORIES

MEETING OF THE BOARD, HELD AT THE REGISTERED

OFFICE OF THE COMPANY ON THURSDAY, THE 10TH.

DAY OF DECEMBER 1936 AT 3 O'CLOCK IN THE AFTERNOON.

PRESENT: Mr. W.H. Haynes (in the Chair).

           Mr. G.S. Hall.

A letter received from Mr. A. Neville Chamberlain,
as follows, was laid on the table:

"Gentlemen,

       For personal reasons, I desire to resign
"my position as Director and Chairman of Directors of
"Hoskins & Son, Ltd. forthwith, and I shall be greatly
"obliged if you will accept my resignation accordingly".

This was considered, and the Chairman was requested
to write that the resignation was accepted with
regret.

W.H.Haynes

CHAIRMAN. 22nd Dec 1936

Neville Chamberlain's political duties gradually took over from his previous commercial responsibilities. During December 1936 Chamberlain, while still Chancellor of the Exchequer, offered his resignation from the Hoskins board. A year later he became Prime Minister. *(Hoskins & Sewell MS, Archives Department, Birmingham Reference Library)*

other members of the Metallic Bedstead Association to assist them with the capture of ships' berth orders. One vital order received in 1936 was the supply of third class and crew accommodation for the *Queen Mary*, for delivery during 1938.

In 1940 Hoskins received a large order from the War Office for mess cupboards. Another order was received from the Ministry of Supply for steel cupboards to store cleaning utensils. Unfortunately, enemy bombing destroyed the wood-working department on the night of 22 November 1940. A few days later, Neville Chamberlain died. The bomb damage seriously disrupted Hoskins' ability to complete their orders and some were relocated to other suppliers.

Hospital bed making became increasingly important to Hoskins' general business after 1945, while ships' berths and government orders continued to decline. Fewer ocean liners were built, as commercial air travel began to compete with them. The requirement for berths declined as new business was principally berths for tnakers and freight vessels. The business in the name of Hoskins & Son was completely reorganised in December 1953, when a new company bearing the name was formed. New trading possibilities were explored and the company decided to fabricate stainless steel articles as a side-line.

Arrangements were made for a merger with Wales Ltd, Atlas Works, Oozells Street, and were ratified in an agreement made in July 1955. Thomas Edmund Wale was the founder of Wales Ltd. He began as a cabinet maker, and by 1883 had included the making of mattresses at his Coventry Road works. Wale & Sons moved their mattress works to Oozells Street in about 1887. They took over the disused Atlas Works, which had been previously used by an engineering firm.

The Atlas Works were located near the entrance to the Birmingham Canal Navigations (BCN) Coal Wharf and occupied a square of land that extended back towards Brasshouse Passage. The full range of mattress and bedstead production became possible when the adjacent Brunswick Bedstead Works was merged with the Atlas Works during, or about, the year 1898. Wales became a limited company in August 1905 and with the capital raised were able to make further extensions to their trade. Thomas Edmund Wale, son William Henry Wale and Frederick Charles Adie were appointed directors of the company.

Wooden bed and cot manufacture was commenced during 1912 when a piece of wharf land was leased from the BCN for the storage of timber. Wales Ltd had a good record of profitability. Each year until 1920 they turned in an increasing profit and shareholders benefited from high dividend payments.

Production now centred on the manufacture of wooden beds, wooden cots, metallic bedsteads, folding beds, wire mattresses, bedding, wire doormats and scrapers. A major extension scheme was planned in 1920, when another share issue was announced. The additional funds were needed to finance the construction of a new factory in Oozells Street North. Additional wharf space was leased from the BNC for the timber business. A subsidiary company, Timberies Ltd, was also formed in 1920, to manage the purchase of hardwood timber for the use of the bedstead departments and also for general sale.

The trade depression that followed the end of the First World War affected the firm's finances just as any other bedstead firm, and thought was given to the sale of the new factory. However, this did not take place and plans were made for other economies. The steam-driven plant that provided power was removed and the works converted to use electricity supplied by Birmingham Corporation.

The Wales Factory, in 1922, had 800,000sq ft of floor space in adjacent buildings of differing ages. Some were freehold, while others were leased from the Colmore Estate. During the 1920s various property purchases were made, where existing buildings adjoined the works.

New products added to the range about this time were day beds and 'Davenports'. The company also started to use Plycene Fabrics on certain products. Further factory alterations were made between 1928 and 1930. The old foundry was replaced by a modern structure that used gas-fired ovens. A drying kiln was installed for the wood yard and new buildings were constructed on the canal wharf. The premises were now at their most extensive. They included offices, 'New' Mill, Wharf Mill, Old Mill, foundry, New Factory, timber wharf, packing department, bedding, assembly department, Top Mill, lathe and polishing shop, paint shop, cot shop and another polishing shop.

The Atlas Works suffered serious bomb damage during the night of 5 November 1940, which left the company with an expensive rebuilding bill. Wooden bed and cot production became the company's major product after the war, with castings left to rust in the foundry. Timberies trade continued to increase, and from 1946 had a semi-independent existence from Wales.

Wales made wooden bedsteads at the Atlas Works following the merger with Hoskins, while production at the Upper Trinity Street works was reorganised. Bed making finally ceased in 1959 and the Atlas Works were closed down. Some staff transferred to the Neptune Works, Upper Trinity Street. The vacant Wales bedstead factory was acquired by Birmingham Corporation in 1960, for conversion into a motor taxation office, record storage and other administrative uses. The Atlas Works were later demolished to make way for the new Brindley Place developments.

Hoskins remained an important supplier of ships' berths and hospital beds, through to the merger with Hoskins & Sewell in 1967. The Upper Trinity Street works became the headquarters of the joint company. The offices at Charlotte Street were closed and all work was transferred back to the centre of Birmingham. The Upper Trinity Street works were rebuilt and remodelled to accommodate the additional work.

The Charles Street factory (which belonged to Hoskins & Sewell) was closed in 1967 and all cabinet work carried out at Upper Trinity Street was transferred to Hay Mills. The Charlotte Street works were finally closed in 1969 and the premises were sold to the neighbouring firm of brass founders, Edwin Showell & Sons Ltd.

Several Birmingham bedstead makers had interests in other business ventures. Few could match the career of Leonard Brierley, who died at his Edgbaston home during October 1904. He was son of Joshua Leonard Brierley, printer and stationer, and was educated at King Edward's Grammar School until the age of thirteen, when he left to assist his father. Leonard then worked for the Birmingham Mint and subsequently became manager of the Marseilles Mint. He returned to Birmingham in 1857 and went into partnership with Mr Greening, bedstead maker. When this partnership was dissolved in 1865, Brierley established his own bedstead works, the Essington Works in Sheepcote Street. He was appointed a JP for Birmingham in 1892. Leonard Brierley was also, at one time, chairman of the Patent Shaft & Axletree Co. Ltd, a partner in John Webb & Co., brass cock founders, Essington Street, a director of Felix Hadley & Co. and a director of the Midland Railway & Carriage Co.

Albert Phillips also had a colourful career. Albert was the son of Philip Phillips, steel pen maker. He was educated at King Edward's Grammar School and later spent several years working at the British consulate in Greece. He then toured India before returning to Birmingham to set up a business in Floodgate Street, making metallic beds. As his business grew, Phillips transferred production to a new works in Rea Street South and then to Eyre Street. He gained an important reputation in the bedstead trade and was regarded as a leader in the industry. He retained his contacts in Greece and became vice-consul and consul for Greece in Birmingham. He was a prominent member of the Jewish community in Birmingham throughout his life.

A new name in the Birmingham bedstead trade came into existence after 1920, when the Crown Bedding Co. took over a disused cycle factory in Charles Henry Street. They began as mattress and bedding makers whose products suited the new wooden bedstead trade. As business improved they moved to new premises at 57 Macdonald Street and then to the factory previously occupied by Bull & Son, Cabinet Maker at 44 Macdonald Street. Their trademark bedding was known as Slumberland and it proved to be a money earner for the company.

Additional premises were acquired during the early 1930s at Tyseley, when Tan Sad Ltd, perambulator makers, vacated their Wharfdale Road works and Crown Bedding took over the premises. They enlarged the Tyseley factory and concentrated work there, closing down the Macdonald Street site.

Slumberland was taken as a company name after 1945, when Tyseley was their headquarters. Various bedstead company mergers followed in the 1950s and 1960s. The business of Charles Bryant was taken into the Slumberland organisation during the period 1966 and 1967. Bryant had specialised in the making of wooden bedsteads and bedroom furniture since the 1940s. By 1968 Bryant's Winson Green factory had been closed and production transferred to other works. Further business rationalisation followed in the 1970s and the Tyseley works were closed during August 1975. Some staff transferred to the Vono works at Tipton.

Another bedstead maker at this period was the Co-op. The CWS had engaged in making bicycles, motor bicycles and some cars; they were flour millers, piano makers and also makers of footwear. During the 1930s they converted their piano works in Belmont Row, which had been built for a cycle fittings maker, into a bedstead works, and it was used in this trade until the early 1960s.

The last bedstead maker in Birmingham was the combined operation of Hoskins & Son and Hoskins & Sewell, Upper Trinity Street, which lasted there until 1996. Here they specialised in making hospital beds and hospital theatre equipment. The company was put into receivership in 1996, but the business was saved and taken over by Huntley Healthcare, and now makes beds as Hoskins Medical Equipment Ltd at Woden Road, Wednesbury.

Slumberland was a brand name adopted by the Crown Bedding Co., and eventually became the company name. Its headquarters were at the former Tan Sad factory, Wharfdale Road, Tyseley. *(Archives Department, Birmingham Reference Library)*

Principal Birmingham Bedstead Makers

Name and Street	Owners	Dates of operation
Aston Lane London Bedstead Works	Thomas Moore, Turner & Moore, Albert Moore, Jeffries & Hoadly	1883–1928
Athole Street Highgate Bedstead Works	James Smith & Son	1872–1912
Balsall Heath Road Speedwell Mills	William Nokes, Phillips & Son	1856–64
Blews Street Apollo Works	Cross, Caddick & Co., Cross & Co., W.A. Cross Ltd	1902–29
Blews Street Britannia Works	Upfill, Morton & Co., Haines & Morton	1863–71
Bolton Street	J. Troman Ltd	1893–1923
Bull Street (26–8)	G. Marris, Marris & Norton	1852–78
Bradford Street Crown Bedstead Works	Greening & Fardon Ltd	1875–81
Bradford Street (123–31)	Davies, Clement & Co.	1879–90
Bradford Street (225)	Benjamin and Josiah Cook	1829–40
Bradford Street (261–4) & Green Street (12)	Benjamin Cook & Son, Benjamin Cook Junior,	1840–82
Bristol Street (11)	William Millward	1861–70
Brueton Street	John Troman	1868–93
Bryant Street, Winson Green	Charles Bryant & Son Ltd	1904–66
Cambridge Street	R.W. Winfield	1827–96
Cato Street North (27–9)	John Talbot	1880–1905
Charlotte Road, Stirchley Midland Bedstead Works	Hoskins & Sewell Ltd	1963–9
Charlotte Street (34) Globe Foundry	Duncan Morrison & Co., Morrison & Crosbie, Crosbie, Marriner & Co., Robert Crosbie	1861–1924
Cheapside (232–5)	Brierley & Geering, Lewis & Philips, James Lewis	1857–78
Cheston Road, Aston	F. Andrews & Co.	1903–23
Eyre Street Excelsior Works	Albert Phillips Ltd	1901–58
George Street West (1) Springhill Foundry	Hooper & Ednam (also trades as Eagle Bedsteads)	1905–23
Glover Street (42) Falcon Works	J.F. Elwell, Charles Wood, Joseph Taylor Bott, Botts Ltd	1871–1912
Glover Street (54)	Hardy & Britain	1878–1900
Granville Street Calcutta Works	Harlow & Co.	1865–71
Granville Street (70, then 52–66)	Edward Phipson, Phipson & Warden	1851–1916
Argylle Works		
Green Street (12–13) Victoria Works	William Robinson	1888–90
Heath Street South Soho Works	James Toy & Son, Tylor & Gilkes, Hoyland & Smith	1860–96
Heath Mill Lane (48)	Crofts & Assinder	1894–1916
Hertford Street City Bedstead Works	Charles Cartwright & Sons	1892–1933
High Street, Bordesley	William Burton & Co.	1829–39
High Street, Bordesley Midland Bedstead Works	Key & Hoskins, Key, Hoskins & Sewell, Hoskins & Sewell	1855–1963
High Street, Bordesley Bordesley Bedstead Works	Harlow & Church, Peyton & Harlow, Peyton & Peyton, Peyton, Hoyland & Barber	1842–1936
Hockley Street (1–4) Star Bedstead Works	John J. Shufflebothan, Star Bedstead Co.	1879–83
Icknield Square/Wellington Street Icknield Metallic Bedstead Works	Hulse & Haines, W. & W.A. Hulse	1864–90

Kings Road, Hay Mills	Frazer Brothers	1900–10
Ledsam Street	Wilson Brothers, Standard Bedstead & Wire Mattress Co. Ltd	1884–1912
Lionel Street (118–25) Lion Works	Fisher, Brown & Co., Fisher, Brown & Bayley	1875–1923
Macdonald Street (46) Anchor Works	W.H. Davis & Co. Ltd	1875–1925
Moseley Street (40–51) Apollo Works	Geering & Leather, H. Geering & Co. Greening & Fardon	1866–81
Moseley Street (136)	Charles Burton	1840–50
Northbrook Street Victoria Works	William Robinson Jnr	1890–1922
Oozells Street (35) Brunswick Works	W. Chambers, William Marrian, Bostock & Marrian, F. Andrews	1855–98
Oozells Street Atlas Works	T.E. Wales, Wales Ltd	1886–1959
Oxford Street (38) Viaduct Works	Samuel Whitfield, S.B. Whitfield	1849–66
Oxford Street (62)	Edward Hatton, Taunton & Hatton, Taunton, Hatton & Johnson	1851–57
Plume Street, Aston	Davis & Mewsom	1913–24
Pritchett Street (88–90) Sultan Works/ Bedford Bedstead Works	Jacob Markes and Co., Fitter Brothers Ltd	1889–1939
Rea Street South Excelsior Works	Albert Phillips	1870–1900
Rea Street South Vaughton Works	Taunton & Hatton, J. & J. Taunton	1857–69
Rea Street South	Wells Brothers	1900–23
Redhill Road Pioneer Works	Tinley Brothers Ltd	1903–33
Rotten Park Street	W. & W.A. Hulse	1890–1926
Sampson Road North	Birmingham Bedstead Co.	1886–93
Sheepcote Street Essington Works	Brierley & Sons Ltd	1866–1930
Sheepcote Street	Thomas Upfill & Son	1860–72
Sherborne Road Belgrave Works	J. & J. Taunton	1869–1936
Sherborne Street Speedwell Works	Phillips & Son Ltd	1866–1919
Sloane Street (7)	Standard Bedstead Co.	1913–32
Springhill, Albion Works	Charles Bryant	1884–1903
Springhill Sterling Works	British Bedstead and Mattress Co.	1925–39
Upper Dean Street Dominion Works	George Gale & Son	1896–1921
Upper Trinity Street	William Burton & Son	1840–5
Upper Trinity Street Neptune Works	Hoskins & Son	1888–1995
Watery Lane Haddon Works	T. Pool & Co.	1897–1921
Watery Lane Gladstone Works	S.B. Whitfield, Whitfield's Bedstead Ltd	1866–1963
Western Road, Soho Works	John Hoyland Ltd	1897–1916
Wharfdale Road, Tyseley	Crown Bedding Co., Slumberland	1933–75
Wiggin Street	Harlow & Co., Frazer Brothers	1875–1902
William Edward Street (48) Vaughton Works	James Tombs	1859–96

CHAPTER FIVE

THE GAS INDUSTRY

MANUFACTURE OF GAS

If coal fuelled the fires of nineteenth-century Birmingham industry, then gas fulfilled this role during the twentieth. Much of the credit for this state of affairs was due to the activities of Birmingham Corporation Gas Department, which continued to update their works and employ the most modern techniques for the production of gas. Local industries benefited from the availability of town gas to fire the furnaces and ovens so necessary for the treatment of metals, the core business of the district.

Town gas was made from coal. It was collected and piped through to lamps for public and private lighting. William Murdoch has received much of the credit for the adoption of gas lighting, when he instituted it at the Soho Foundry in 1802. Elsewhere contemporaries of Murdoch were responsible for gas lighting being introduced to selected premises across the country. Each new use proved the advantages of coal gas for lighting, but commercial production of gas for public lighting proved a difficult hurdle to overcome, especially with regard to the safe conveyance of gas to the user. Some ten years later these problems had been overcome and the first companies were established for gas making for public and industrial purposes. London was a leader in the development of the public gas supply, with the building of a gas works in 1812. Birmingham was there too, when John Gosling established a gas works on vacant land near Broad Street in 1817.

Private companies frequently provided the finance for the gas-making ventures, although some municipal undertakings were also formed to supply town gas. The principles of gas making involved the heating of coal in retorts, by a process known as carbonisation, and the collection of the gas for sale. A lucrative by-product industry developed as gas supply increased. Coke, coal tar, cyanides and ammoniacal liquor all came to be used elsewhere. Cokes were suited for iron smelting, chain making and a variety of foundries. Tar was taken by the distillers to be refined into a host of compounds that ranged from creosote and naptha to phenol and aniline dyes. Cyanides had an increasing importance once a plastics industry had been developed, while ammoniacal liquor proved to be good source of sulphates for artificial manure production.

Commercial gas making in Birmingham was in the hands of two firms, the Birmingham Gas Light & Coke Co. and the Birmingham & Staffordshire Gas Light Co., the original works of which were situated at Swan Village, West Bromwich. Some Birmingham firms also operated private gas-making plants to supply their needs and the Birmingham Workhouse at Winson Green also had a canal-side gas works.

Gas-making plants had several standard features. Coal was burned in retorts housed in a substantial retort house, or houses. Gas was then passed to the purifying house, where it was passed through lime, and later iron oxide. This process removed much of the hydrogen sulphide content and generally improved the composition of the gas. It was then stored in holders located around the site and passed to the consumers via the meter house.

Demand for gas increased when it was adapted for heating and cooking purposes. Businesses and private homes were linked to the works through a network of mains, which continued to expand with urban and industrial development.

GAS WORKS IN BIRMINGHAM

Works	Period of Use	Notes
Adderley Street	1842–1940	Also known as the Pagoda Works. Owned by Birmingham & Staffordshire Gas Light, until 1875, and subsequently Birmingham Corporation. The gas holders remained on site until 1959.
Fazeley Street	1837–80	Established by the Birmingham Gas Light & Coke Co. and taken over by Birmingham Corporation during 1875. They had a brief working existence for Birmingham Corporation and were leased to Fellows Morton & Co., canal carriers, who adapted part of the site for the canal carrying trade.
Gas Street	1817–50	Established by John Gosling 1817. It became the Birmingham Gas Light& Coke Co. The gas holders were retained for several years after closure of the gas making plant.
Nechells	1900–69	Built for Birmingham Corporation, these works were established on the opposite side of the Midland Railway to the existing Saltley Gas Works. They were renamed Nechells (West) after the take-over by West Midlands Gas Board in 1949.
Saltley	1857–1969	Owned by Birmingham & Staffordshire Gas Light until 1875, and subsequently Birmingham Corporation. Became known as Nechells (East) Gas Works after plant was taken over by the West Midlands Gas Board in 1949.
Windsor Street	1847–1974	Constructed for the Birmingham Gas Light & Coke Co. Ltd and passed to Birmingham Corporation in 1875. These works were extensively rebuilt between 1880 and 1887. They were acquired by the West Midlands Gas Board in 1949 and were the last in Birmingham to produce coal gas.

Joseph Chamberlain and his team of councillors were responsible for the takeover of the private gas making ventures for the general benefit of the town, and instituted a bill in Parliament for the purchase of the two local gas-making companies. Birmingham Corporation acquired four commercial gas-making plants in Birmingham, and the Swan Village Works, during 1875. Gas production at the Fazeley Street Works was gradually phased out and finally ended in 1880, leaving the other works to be enlarged and modified. Considerable improvements were made to the gas-making plants at Adderley Street, Saltley and Windsor Street. The original retort houses fitted with a type of horizontal retort were replaced with larger retort houses for increased production.

Coal for gas making was first obtained from local mines in the Black Country, which was brought by canal boat. It was eventually found that better illuminating power was obtained from Derbyshire, Nottinghamshire, North Wales and Yorkshire coals. Railways became integral to the movement of gas coals to Birmingham gas works. Yearly contracts were arranged with the colliery owners for the delivery of coals to the gas works and orders were frequently split between mines. Each year mine owners tendered quotes that included rail carriage from the pit in their wagons. Birmingham Corporation Gas Committee then sifted through the tenders to select those that best suited their needs. Cost was an important factor, but the quality of gas coals was also considered.

Thousands of tons of coal were moved each week to the Birmingham gas works and the handling of wagon-load coal involved the construction of private sidings. An extensive fleet of railway wagons was amassed by the Gas Department to carry the coals from the mines to the works. Contracts with a number of different railway wagon makers were arranged for hire and maintenance, but gradually ownership of the fleet passed to the Gas Department. Wagon maintenance stayed with the wagon builders, and several contracts remained in force with different firms across the country.

Saltley Gas Works and Swan Village Gas Works were the first to have rail access. Saltley Gas Works had been built beside the Midland Railway so that gas coals might be delivered by rail. Horses were used to move the coal wagons around the works. Birmingham Corporation Gas Committee decided to improve the Saltley Works, and increase gas making, through the building of a new retort house, a new purifying house and railway sidings that were worked by locomotives. Work on the extensions was completed during 1877, and the first Corporation-owned railway locomotive commenced work in the sidings.

The No. 1 and No. 2 Retort Houses at Saltley were demolished between 1901 and 1902 to make way for an improved gas-making plant. The new No. 1 and No. 2 Retort House block occupied a rectangular strip of land near the Midland Railway Co. main line. In this building inclined retorts were installed. During 1908 a new coke-handling plant was constructed, complete with coke conveyors and railway loading screens. The pair of Midland Railway wagons are standing on the track leading to the coke screen. *(Birmingham Gas Department Magazine)*

Nechells Gas Works,
c. 1928. Nechells was the
last carbonisation plant to
be built for Birmingham
Corporation.
*(Birmingham Gas
Department Magazine)*

Women workers at the Oxide Plant, Nechells Gas Works. The shortage of male workers during the First World War led to women adopting many male-dominated roles. From ammunition workers to bus drivers, women filled the places of the men. Some duties were harder than others and one of the worst was working at the oxide crusher. Spent oxide from the gas purifiers was removed and crushed before it was sent to the chemical works. *(Birmingham Gas Department Magazine)*

Attention was then given to the improvement of the Windsor Street Works. The gas works in Windsor Street had a block of three retort houses situated beside the Birmingham & Fazeley Canal, which were exclusively served by canal boats. During 1880 a new branch railway was completed for the London & North Western Railway to Aston goods and sidings adjoining Rupert Street, which provided rail access to Windsor Street Gas Works for the first time. Coal was conveyed from Rupert Street Sidings to the 'Old' Retort House along a temporary narrow gauge tramway. Meanwhile plans were made for improvement and enlargement of the gas works. A new, and larger, retort house, in Avenue Road, was commissioned. It was built between 1885 and 1887 and involved the construction of a high-level railway that reached the retort house on raised piers. Six ranges of a new type of horizontal retort were installed to provide the gas, and each was charged mechanically with coal received from the railway wagons.

In 1892 Birmingham Corporation Gas Department opened a new set of railway sidings that served a coke store in Devon Street. This site was later incorporated in the totally new gas-making plant, Nechells, which was completed between 1899 and 1901. Nechells Gas Works had sidings that connected with both the Midland Railway and the London & North Western Railway.

Adderley Street Gas Works was never directly supplied by railway, but the works lay close to the Midland Railway, Lawley Street goods station, and coal was carted through the streets to the works. A new retort house was completed at Adderley Street during 1908, the basic fabric of which still survives. Horses were extensively employed to haul the coal carts to Adderley Street Gas Works, and stables for them, built on the site of a pair of old gas holders, were provided at Barn Street. An experimental road train was put on trial in 1911 to move coal from Lawley Street to Adderley Street. Built and supplied by the Daimler Co., the unit comprised a tractor and wooden-bodied wagons. The experiment had mixed results and was the cause of complaint by factory owners on the route when the train began to operate. A complaint from Imperial Enamel, in Watery Lane, led to the road train being made to pass their works at 1 mile an hour. Meanwhile, horse haulage continued to be used.

Other schemes to improve transport access to the Adderley Street Gas Works included use of the tramway lines from Camp Hill goods station. The suggestion that Birmingham Corporation Tramways would carry coal in wagons on their tram tracks involved the construction of a siding along Bowyer Street to the gas works. The idea failed to be implemented, and road transport continued to be the only means of serving the Adderley Street Gas Works. Fordson tractors pulling trailers eventually replaced horse haulage on the mile-long haul from Lawley Street, until the gas works finally ceased operation in April 1940.

The demand for gas continued to increase throughout the nineteenth century. Birmingham Corporation supplied 2,327.6 million cu ft of gas in 1875. By 1901 production had risen to a yearly make of 5,709.6 million cu ft. The initial demand for gas lighting was supplemented by domestic demand for heating and cooking, while the needs of industry inspired new requirements for gas-fired ovens or for driving a new form of power, the gas engine.

Land was purchased in 1901 at Birches Green, Erdington, for a new gas works. A public enquiry followed and the scheme received so much opposition that it was shelved. Ten years later, in 1911, the annual gas production had now reached 7,693.9 million cu ft and a new site, at Washwood Heath, was considered. Land for the works was acquired from the Drainage Board, but construction was delayed through the onset of the First World War. Once hostilities had ceased the generation of electricity had become paramount and plans for a new retort house, purifying house and connecting sidings were shelved. The land was, however, used for the erection of gas holders and a railway wagon repair depot.

Gas works provided employment for a range of skills. A number of labouring jobs were needed in what was essentially a male domain. Judging from the weekly accident reports, working in the gas works was not without risk of physical injury. Some labourers were employed as coal and coke wheelers and loaders, others were machinemen, firemen and stokers, and all workers were prone to receive knocks, bumps and burns. Their jobs included unloading of coal wagons into wheelbarrows, taking the coal to the retorts, and the carriage of coke away to railway wagons or canal boats. Stokers and firemen fed the furnaces, raked out the coke and cleaned out the ashes.

The stoker's job was physically demanding, particularly with regard to the horizontal and inclined retorts. William Freeman's recollections published in the *Gas Department*

Magazine, 1935, reveal the harsh nature of the job. Freeman was employed at Windsor Street Gas Works between 1892 and 1935. He started work at the 'Old' Retort House, when the shift pattern changed from twelve hours to eight hours and extra men were required for the additional shift. Pay was the princely sum of 4*s* a shift. 'There were then both horizontal through retorts and stop enders on the Works, and the whole of the Retort House work was done by hand.' Freeman became a 'shovel' charger, which required skill and experience with the shovel. The charges for the retorts had to be level and tapered towards the mouthpiece, where the gas was drawn off. The conditions of smoke and flaming heat made work unpleasant. Discharging coke was done by hand rakes in extremely hot conditions. The men were quickly drenched in perspiration when performing this task. Each worker was expected to rake out the coal from thirty-six retorts and look after three fires each shift. The New Retort House, in Avenue Road, had machine charging, and all discharged coke fell to the cellar. Machine charging and pushing out did not put an end to the hand raking out of the retorts, as the machine was unable to push out all the retorts, and it was left for the men to get coke out. Coke from the New Retort House was quenched, and then forked into barrows that were run to either the boats or the railway wagons. Barrowloads of coke from the No. 1 and No. 4 cellars at Windsor Street were run through narrow subways lit by gas flares.

Coke transport was later improved through the introduction of skips running along a runway or light railway track. Freeman thought the horses used on this task had a very rough time. 'It was nothing to see a horse, when the trolley jammed in the points, pulled right off his feet, and I have seen horses work for 32 hours without a break, and also horses work for weeks at a time with only 16 hours break.'

Pay day was frequently an excuse for drink. Freeman recalled these times as follows:

Pay-time was Friday night in these old days, and the men had done their first draw before 10 o'clock, were paid, and allowed out of the Works until 11 p.m. They then bought in their two-gallon jars of beer for consumption during the remainder of the shift. Friday, Saturday and Sunday nights were considered to be lively. Several fights usually took place on these nights, and I have seen as many as four draws of coke in the cellar, one on top of the other, waiting to be removed, when the men were in a fit condition to carry out the work. I must say, however that this coke was always cleared up before the men went home. One pitiable aspect of the conditions in these days was to see wives and children hanging around the gate on Friday and Saturday nights with the hope of getting some money from the men to carry on the household.

Ascension pipes carried the gas away for treatment and purification. Pipe men were employed to maintain the pipes and the associated valves, which were subject to blockages from tar and other substances. They were in regular danger of receiving burns. The movement of railway wagons around the site involved the Gas Department with the ownership and maintenance of steam railway locomotives. A team of drivers and shunters were employed as well as fitters and cleaners for the day-to-day maintenance. There were also steam-powered

Retorts for burning coal to collect the gas took various forms. The sight common in many gas works was a bank of retorts arranged neatly in a brick wall, behind which was the furnace used for heating them. Each retort had its own ascension tube that collected the gas and carried it through a network of pipes to the purifiers. *(Heartland Press Collection)*

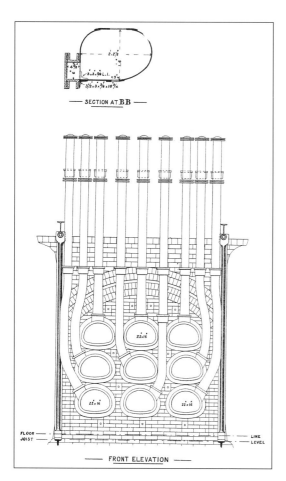

cranes and stationary steam engines and boilers on site, and all required engine drivers and maintenance. Salaried staff included clerks to keep account of the coal deliveries and the sales of coke and by-products.

The provision of gas mains and maintenance of the gas supply occupied the attention of another group of workers and inspectors. New gas mains continued to be laid with the growth of the city of Birmingham, and the demand was not limited by the city boundaries. Gas was also supplied to areas such as Sutton Coldfield and beyond. Gas passed from the holders was at a pressure sufficient for local supply. Longer distances, such as to Kings Norton, involved a system of compressors, high-pressure mains and governors. Windsor Street Gas Works had three large steam-powered compressors that delivered gas to the high-pressure main to Kings Norton, where a governor then reduced the pressure for customer use.

There was also the sale and fitting of gas meters and appliances, which were kept at Windsor Street. Birmingham Corporation decided to concentrate the department here when they took over the works and transferred a similar facility here from Saltley. Gas meters were made at Windsor Street, but the bulk of the stock was purchased from other suppliers. These premises were completely rebuilt during 1937, and replaced by a new three-storey office and repair block that faced both Windsor Street and Lord Street.

List of shops and shops stores passing through Lord Street in twelve months
(*City of Birmingham Gas Department Magazine*, Summer 1937, vol. 17, no. 6)

Meters Reconditioned 21,000

Cookers and fires, and other apparatus reconditioned 20,000

New domestic appliances of various kinds tested for accuracy and safety 37,000

Prepayment and ordinary meters made to Department's own design 2,800

Prepayment and ordinary meters issued from the stores 40,000

Prepayment and ordinary meters returned from consumers for repair and renovation 30,000

New meters received and handled from manufacturers 15,000

Permanent hire fires and hire purchase fires, radiators, boilers cookers, and geysers, and sale outright of fires boilers, cookers etc issued from Lord Street 31,000

Prepayment and Permanent Hire Cookers sent out 18,000

Prepayment and permanent hire cookers etc returned for repair and renovation 20,000

Appliances received in and issued from stores 79,000

Parts issued from depot for repair and renovation 220,000

The need for obtaining the best quality gas coals led to the establishment of a testing plant. A large-scale coal testing works beside the Nechells Gas Works was commenced in 1905. The plant included the installation of horizontal retorts and condensing, exhausting and purifying plant, and was in every sense a complete gas works in its own right. These works also became the testing bed for new retort design, tar towers and other gas-making technology.

A twentieth-century development, and economy, was the water gas plant, where white-hot cokes were used to break up steam to produce a mix of hydrogen and carbon monoxide gas. In this form, the gas mixture was unsatisfactory for lighting purposes, but the lighting properties improved when mixed with an extract of petroleum, or gas oil. Water gas plants were installed at both Nechells and Windsor Street, where the water gas was mixed with the coal gas to form a final gas supply mix.

Such was the varying quality of gas coals supplied for carbonisation that testing coal and examining methods of charging was essential for any gas undertaking. Birmingham Corporation installed a special plant at Nechells where the regular task of testing coal for carbonisation was undertaken. The plant included a bank of horizontal retorts, installed when the plant opened in 1905. Experiments to improve gas making included trials with vertical retorts. During 1911 a set of Dessau retorts (centre left) were built. One year later another set of vertical retorts to the Woodall Duckham design (centre right) were erected. *(Birmingham Gas Department Magazine)*

Commercial production of water gas began in the USA, and it was not until 1891 that the first British plant was installed at Beckton Gas Works, London. During 1892 another water gas plant was erected at Belfast, to the designs of Arthur Glasgow and Alexander Humphreys, and it was these gentlemen who came to later supply water gas plants to Birmingham. Considerable improvements had been made to the manufacturing plant and the advantages of water gas as a coal gas additive were then appreciated. The water gas plant was cheaper to install and occupied less space than a normal gas-making plant. It also could also be put into operation at short notice.

The Nechells water gas plant was located in Devon Street next to the coke store. It was brought into use during 1896, when the new plant was classed as part of the Saltley Works. Water gas making employed fewer staff than the normal gas retorts, and with improvements in technology lent itself to automation. By the 1930s Windsor Street plant had three automatic Humphreys & Glasgow machines and one hand-operated machine. Each water gas production machine comprised a fan, charger, generator, carburettor, superheater and washer. The fan was required to blow air periodically through the coke as part of the first run. The air passing through the generator chamber caused the already hot cokes to burn to white heat, raising the temperature ready for the next phase, the 'up run'. With this phase the air was shut off and steam was forced up through the base of the generator and passed through the coke. The gas generated was called 'blue water gas' and this was sent through a washer to a holder. During a third phase gas oil was sprayed from the top of the carburettor and the gases produced followed the blue water gas into the holder. The resulting mix of 'cracked oil' and blue water gas made a hydrogen-rich gas, commonly referred to as 'carburetted water gas'. Further blue water gas was extracted in the 'back run' phase, where the flow of steam was reversed and passed back through the superheater and carburettor to the generator, before the cycle was started again.

An increasing demand for gas kept a select group of Gas Department engineers in constant search of improvement. They were keen to take up any new development in Britain and throughout Europe. A large number of the existing gas retorts were of the horizontal type. Nechells No. 1 retort house had inclined retorts, which were then considered state-of-the-art technology. During 1909 Gas Department representatives looked at advances in horizontal retorts, newly devised vertical retorts and chamber ovens. Various gas works were visited and trials were conducted before resources were committed. By 1912 the Gas Department was ready to make changes. Woodall-Duckham & Co. won the contract to install two ranges of a new vertical retort plant at Windsor Street Gas Works during 1912.

Another development was the construction of coke ovens at Saltley. The No. 3 Retort House at Saltley had been built in 1861, but the retorts were now considered worn out and ready for replacement. The Gas Department chose to replace the building with a bank of chamber ovens. The purchase of a trial bank of twelve Kopper chamber ovens was authorised in 1912 and a new order for another fifty-four ovens was placed shortly afterwards. The plant was completed during 1914.

The Saltley chamber ovens were a new development for a British commercial gas works. Ovens of this type were frequently used for the production of coke (for steelworks) and the gas produced was considered a by-product to be collected for electricity generation or heating purposes. Birmingham now chose to use a plant to make gas for lighting purposes. At the same time, a better quality coke could be made and sold. 'Mond', or 'producer', gas was burned to provide heat for the Saltley ovens. Mond gas was a type of coal gas made from poorer quality of coals that was developed for industrial purposes. The producers were fed with coal, which was burned, and the resulting gas was passed through a recovery tower in which a sulphuric acid-rich liquor percolated down and removed the ammonia as ammonium sulphate.

Coal was fed into the chamber ovens by a travelling stamping and charging machine. Each oven was charged in turn with crushed coal that was delivered to the ovens by

A section through the coke oven, showing the charging machine on the left and discharging arrangement on the right, where coke from the ovens was loaded into either railway wagons or canal boats. *(Journal of Gas Lighting and Water Supply, June 1913)*

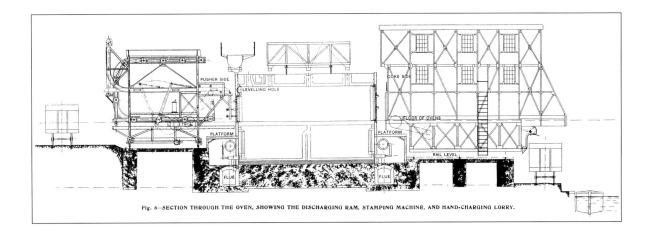

Fig. 6—SECTION THROUGH THE OVEN, SHOWING THE DISCHARGING RAM, STAMPING MACHINE, AND HAND-CHARGING LORRY.

Saltley coke plant, *c.* 1928. Birmingham Corporation was keen to keep its gas making to the most up-to-date methods. The construction of coke ovens at Saltley, adjacent to the existing carbonisation plant, was an innovative concept aimed at supplying a better quality of coke in addition to making coal gas for town use. The plant included charging machines, coke ovens and coke quenchers for the collection of the coke. *(Birmingham Gas Department Magazine)*

Female workers at the sulphate of ammonia plant during the First World War. The Saltley works had a Mond gas plant that burned cheaper quality coals to make the gas to fire the coke ovens. A by-product was ammonium sulphate, which was collected for making into fertiliser. *(Birmingham Gas Department Magazine)*

railway wagon. Coke was discharged at the opposite end of the furnace by an electrically driven dram into a 'Goodall' coke quencher. Kopper's was a German firm, but had an agency in Sheffield that supplied the ovens and fittings. The Mond gas-making plant was the scene of a terrible explosion in April 1923, in which one worker was killed and several injured.

Birmingham Corporation Gas Department assisted the war effort during the First World War through a determined push to supply gas to industry, which included the new munitions works. A Toluol plant was also commissioned at Nechells Gas Works during April 1915. This plant made Benzol and Toluol, which were used in the manufacture of the high explosives TNT, Lyddite and Ammonol.

By 1919 another four ranges of vertical retorts were built at Windsor Street, completely replacing the earlier horizontal retort facility. Vertical retorts, supplied by the Vertical Retort Syndicate, were also put into the No. 2 retort house at Nechells during 1913. Nechells No. 1 retort house was rebuilt during 1922 to take Woodham-Duckham Vertical Retorts and went into full production the following year. Saltley retort house received similar treatment in 1928.

The complete changeover to vertical retorts had been a lengthy process, but the long conversion period was needed to accomplish the finance and the extensive required changes in plant and equipment. Gas production in vertical retorts was a continuous process in which coal of a particular size was fed into the top. Coal wagons were turned upside down in a rotary tipper and the lumps of coal were fed to a coal crusher. A gravity

Vertical retorts eventually became the standard for gas carbonisation. With every conversion, production of gas was increased. Saltley Gas Works was converted during 1928, when production was increased to 7 million cu ft of gas per day. Alderman Gregory is shown charging the first retort during the official ceremony to mark the conversion. *(Birmingham Gas Department Magazine)*

Avenue Road retort house, Windsor Street Gas Works. The reconstruction of the Windsor Street Gas Works was carried out during the 1880s, when the existing retort houses and gas holders were pulled down to be replaced by a completely new carbonisation plant. The new retort house was built on a wide strip of land beside the canal. *(Heartland Press Collection)*

A general view of the Windsor Street Gas Works as seen from the offices in Windsor Street, 1938. In the foreground is the roof of the stores, a relief gas holder. From the centre left is the high level railway, condenser and exhauster houses, condensers (in the centre) and No. 12 gas holder, while to the rear of these structures are the retort house, purifiers and the No. 13 and No. 14 gas holders. *(Heartland Press Collection)*

bucket elevator then carried the crushed coal to the top of the ovens and a tipping tray conveyor, which fed the coal into hoppers that discharged into the retorts. Coke was mechanically removed from the base, and as it was taken away fresh coal was fed in at the top. The hot cokes dropped into skips, or wagons, that were hauled or pushed out of the retort house to the coke storage yard or screening plant. Staffing the vertical retorts required the creation of a new method of working. Labourers were assigned to posts as Top Floor, Middle Floor and Bottom Floor. Included their numbers were the tar pot men, scurfers and firemen.

Birmingham gas works continued to supply both the needs of Birmingham industry and domestic purposes through the inter-war years. New housing increased demand for gas appliances, such as fires, cookers and meters. The biggest test for the Birmingham Gas Department came during the Second World War, when the demands of wartime industry achieved an unprecedented high. The Gas Department coped, despite the closure of Adderley Street Gas Works, by running all the carbonisation and water gas plants to full capacity. By 1945 the annual make of gas exceeded 20,000 million cu ft. Manufacture of Benzol and Toluol for conversion to TNT and other explosives was recommenced at the four gas works, and town gas was used to top up barrage balloons, owing to a shortage of hydrogen gas. The extensive Gas Board wagon fleet became part of a national pooled fleet, and the Washwood Heath Wagon Works took on the task of general maintenance for wagons from the pool.

The return to peacetime after 1945 presented the Birmingham Gas Department with new challenges, particularly with the specialised heat treatment of metals, but their independent control was to be short lived. The nationalisation of the British gas industry followed in 1949, and all Birmingham gas works became the property of the West Midlands Gas Board. It was a critical time for the local gas industry. Before nationalisation, gas was supplied to the West Midlands by twenty-two local authorities and forty-nine private companies that owned a total of seventy-three manufacturing locations. The Birmingham & District Division became responsible for gas-making plants in Birmingham at Windsor Street, Nechells and Saltley, as well as another two at Solihull and Henley-in-Arden.

A programme of rationalisation was introduced, where some plants were closed down and mains were linked up with other undertakings. This link-up took several years to complete, but by 1958 new mains were laid across the district and gas flow was managed from a control centre at Lord Street.

Tower purifiers were installed at Nechells to improve gas making there and were only the second of this type to be constructed in Britain. The installation was to comprise twelve towers, and the first set of six towers, together with a stocking tower and stocking frame, were put to work in January 1949. Each tower was 61ft high and had the capacity to hold fourteen containers of iron oxide, which were replaced from the stocking tower when the oxide was spent. These new purifying towers had been commenced before the takeover by the Gas Board and proved to be the last major improvement to the Birmingham coal carbonisation plants.

Any future developments were to be made elsewhere. The Gas Board decided to make improvements to a number of selected sites, which included new retort houses at Swan Village and Walsall and modern carburetted water gas plants at several Black Country locations.

In addition to the Birmingham gas works, the Gas Board also acquired a modern gas works at Solihull. The Solihull Gas Works had been established by Solihull Gas Co. in 1869 and came to supply the local area. They had absorbed Knowle and District Gas Co. in 1935, and during the mid-1950s had taken over the supply to Henley-in-Arden. The demands of supplying the nearby Shadow Aircraft Factory had resulted in complete reconstruction of the gas works with vertical retorts. Solihull Gas Works were closed in 1962, the year before a new gas-making plant at Coleshill was commissioned.

Construction of the Coleshill gas-making plant had been delayed through difficulties in obtaining planning permission, and when the works opened in July 1963 the plant was already outdated. The new works made gas from low-grade coal by the Lurgi process, a method that derives its name from the German firm that devised the process. Rail sidings connected with the British Railways Birmingham–Leicester line. Even when construction was underway for the Coleshill plant, plans were being made for a natural gas pipeline across the country from Canvey Island. Methane, or natural gas, from the Sahara desert was to be delivered by boat in liquid form from Algeria and reconverted to gas for pumping along the pipeline that served the South East, the Midlands and the North West.

The 1960s were therefore changing times for the gas industry, and the days of coal carbonisation were numbered. The tide of gas works closures continued, but four sites (Coleshill, Stourbridge, Swan Village and Wolverhampton) were adapted as peak load gas-making plants that made gas from oil or naptha. Natural gas was first supplied to the Birmingham district during 1968, when the Coleshill Works became the first high pressure reforming plant. Another two reforming plants were constructed at Tipton and Washwood Heath.

Conversion to natural gas was accompanied by modification of appliances to burn the methane gas. Consumption of gas was changing. Its use in public lighting had declined while use of gas cookers and gas heaters grew. A new market was gas central heating,

With the substitution of natural gas for coal gas all the infrastructure associated with coal carbonisation and water gas making was removed. Facilities associated with distribution had a much longer life. Some gas holders remain skyline features, and are used to store gas for peak demand. Windsor Street Gas Works still have three gas holders (Nos 12 to 14) and a service depot. The buildings remaining include the former compressor and exhauster house, fitting and blacksmiths' shops. The blacksmiths' shop, which is located in the buildings closest to the No. 12 gas holder, was kept to provide for the continuing need for smiths' work in the modern gas industry, April 2000. *(Ray Shill)*

which became popular after the imposition of the Clean Air Act. The changeover, for Birmingham, entailed a total of eight years. A familiar street-side sight during these times was the burners that were employed to burn off the coal gas from the mains before they were flushed through with natural gas. The last conversion took place at Bracken Road, Erdington on 16 August 1976.

The decline of the coal carbonisation industry from the 1960s onwards was hastened through the discovery of new sources of natural gas. A vast supply of natural gas was found in the North Sea and developed during the 1970s, the gas being delivered ashore at Peterhead into the main network serving the whole country.

Windsor Street was the last working coal carbonisation plant in the West Midlands. Production ceased in February 1974. The Gas Board retained the site as offices and workshops. The gasholders and distribution system were also kept as part of the supply chain to customers.

The closure of the gas carbonisation works had a significant impact on industry. Mines, which had benefited from the supply of gas coals, were without a lucrative market. By-product manufacturers that included the tar distillers and fertilizer makers had lost an important sector in their supply chain. Retort makers and firebrick makers also lost out. Closures of mines, firebrick works and tar distilleries followed. Most cannot deny the benefits derived from natural gas, and few will mourn the loss of the smell around the gas works or the lethal effects of prolonged exposure to coal gas. Yet the legacy of lost jobs throughout the region cannot be ignored, particularly as they came at a time when other local industries were contracting or leaving the area.

Not all premises were served by the public gas works; some factories installed private gas-making plants, and a smaller version was produced in Birmingham suited to large houses and public institutions. *(Heartland Press Collection)*

MANUFACTURE OF GAS EQUIPMENT

Birmingham held the honours not only for gas lighting, but also for the invention of the gas meter, without which the system could not have become a practical success. William Murdoch was the first to bring coal gas into public use and it was his assistant, Samuel Clegg, who invented the gas meter. Clegg went into partnership with Samuel Crossley at a factory in Cottage Lane, City Road, London; the firm was known as S. & J. Crossley. W. Parkinson acquired the business during 1847, and it was a firm of Parkinson who brought part of the trade back to Birmingham in 1890 with the purchase of the meter business of J. Bent & Son in Bell Barn Road.

J. Bent & Son had commenced making meters in 1830. A second Birmingham factory, in Stour Street, was acquired in 1897 from John Sheldon. The premises there included a malleable iron foundry, known as the Newport Foundry. Parkinson & Co. was already making gas stoves, and it was decided to transfer the Parkinson foundry and gas stove departments there.

W. Parkinson merged with the firm of W. & B. Cowan (of Edinburgh & Manchester) in November 1900 to form Parkinson & W. & B. Cowan Ltd. This firm became the parent company when it was decided to separate the meter trade from gas stove manufacture. Parkinson Stove Co. Ltd, based in Stour Street, was formed during November 1907. Gas meter production remained under the direct control of the parent

John Bent & Son,
advertisement.

Below: Parkinson & W.B.
Cowan Ltd. made gas
meters in Birmingham at
the former John Bent
factory in Bell Barn Road.
Its products ranged from
meters that measured
household gas to the large
station ones that recorded
gas sent out from the
works. *(Heartland Press
Collection)*

company until 1925, when Parkinson & Cowan Gas Meter Ltd was formed. Gas meter production was carried on at various sites in London, Birmingham, Edinburgh and Manchester. The Birmingham factory remained at 283–9 Bell Barn Road.

Birmingham had several firms engaged in meter production, and some came into the trade with the demands of new housing and urban growth from 1920. Firms such as Parkinson produced meters of various sizes ranging from the enormous station meters that measured the gas passing from the works, down to the smaller meters used to record industrial and domestic consumption. The domestic type came to be made in two versions. One simply recorded the amount used, and meter readers would come along to read the figures and arrange for the customer bill. The other type was the auto-meter, which took coins and allowed the supply of a specific amount of gas. The Birmingham Gas Department at Windsor Street Gas Works made, repaired and supplied both types of meter. Each one had to be tested for accuracy and sealed before supply to the customer. Meter testing came under the jurisdiction of the magistrates. Birmingham had testing stations at Moor Street and later at Sheep Street. A testing sub-station was later provided for the exclusive use of Birmingham Gas Department at Lord Street.

The Parkinson Stove Co. took over the Maughan Patent Geyser Co. in about 1912 and built a geyser factory in Morville Street. A new foundry was also erected between 1913 and 1914 at Stechford, on land bounded by Station Street and a new road, First Avenue. The move to Stechford was part of the town planning initiative of Birmingham Corporation, which had gained Stechford from Worcestershire as a result of boundary changes of 1911. A railway siding was laid to the foundry with the sanction of an agreement made with the London & North Western Railway in November 1912. It was the first Parkinson factory in Birmingham to be served by rail, and this link proved useful when the Stechford foundry was given over to munitions work during the First World War. From 1919, Parkinson's established a number of different departments at Stechford, which in addition to the foundry included a press shop, pickling shop, paint shop, enamel shop and cooker assembly. Stour Street Works were closed and all cooker making was transferred there.

An important part of the Stechford works was the track. The track was used for gas cooker assembly, and workers fitted various parts to the cookers as they proceeded along the track. The press shop supplied pressed metal work that was painted and lacquered on site before being sent to the track. The foundry was closed, as an economy measure, in about 1968. Castings and other parts were then supplied by other firms, and were brought into the stores for supply to track as required. Meanwhile, the old foundry buildings were converted to a store for packing and cardboard. Parkinson gas cookers were popular with householders, but one design made at Stechford had less success. This was the unusual combination of an electric and gas cooker, which had electric hobs and a gas-fired grill.

Parkinson & Co.,
Stour Street Works.
*(Birmingham Arts &
Industry Magazine)*

Gas stove fitting shop,
Parkinson, Cowan & Co.,
Birmingham. Parkinson,
Cowan concentrated as
stove making at the Stour
Street Works, Ladywood,
from 1897. *(Birmingham
Arts & Industry Magazine)*

The Stechford works came to occupy some 27 acres, and incorporated the public streets in the site. Parkinson, Cowan eventually became part of the Thorn EMI Group, who also owned Tricity, Moffat and Bendix. The Stechford works retained a large workforce through to 1987, when the business was taken over by AB Electrolux. Union representatives immediately raised concern for the works, as job losses were feared. They had already had dealings with Electrolux when it had taken over White's Consolidated Corporation works and had instituted large-scale redundancies before a management buy-out saved the remaining work force.

Main entrance to Parkinson, Cowan factory, Stechford, 1992. The Parkinson, Cowan works at Stechford was laid out around a group of streets which were eventually incorporated into the factory site as the works were enlarged. *(Ray Shill)*

Below, left: Office block built for the Parkinson Stove Co. in 1919, seen in 1992. Plans for building a new foundry for Parkinson's were approved before the First World War. The task of construction went ahead, but with the onset of war the Stechford factory was converted for munitions work. Following the end of hostilities stove making was concentrated at Stechford, when the office block was completed. *(Ray Shill)*

Below, right: Parkinson, Cowan gate sign, Station Road, Stechford, 1992. *(Ray Shill)*

Electrolux commenced a programme of works rationalisation, and shed about half the workforce by 1991. The final blow came in November 1991, when the workers were told the factory would close at the end of the year. On the same day the closure was announced, Prime Minister John Major stated in the House of Commons that there was a 'sharp slow down' in the rise of unemployment. The sceptical leader of the opposition, Neil Kinnock, told Mr Major that his policies were putting people out of work. Despite the efforts of local MP Terry Davis, the Stechford factory closed and the site was sold off for redevelopment. Most of the buildings, and the Parkinson Cowan Club, were demolished to make way for a new retail park. Cooker production was transferred to the Electrolux factory in Spennymoor, County Durham.

The Birmingham and the Black Country became the hub of the British gas stove making industry and supplied stoves worldwide from works that included Arden Hill, Cannon (of Coseley), Parkinson's and Wright's. Demands for gas cookers grew during the First World War, when the stove trade was required to supply the munitions factories with heating and cooking plant. Subsequently this trade was continued with the supply of cooking facilities for works canteens.

John Wright came from Ongar, in Essex, to Birmingham to set up a gas stove and gas cooker factory during 1866. His works were first located at 35 Albion Street, but within three years larger premises were acquired at 30 (later 71) Broad Street. Wright quickly gained a reputation for a new range of gas cookers. Early cookers were made with a single cast-iron case. With Wright's model there was a double shell, comprising an outside iron shell and an inside enamelled sheet metal case separated from the iron by a layer of asbestos to conserve the heat. Another important part of their trade was gas-fired heaters, known as 'radiating gas stoves'. These circular stoves were portable and were linked to the gas supply through a flexible tube. They were used in a variety of public, domestic and industrial locations and were supplied in an assortment of sizes that ranged in height from 21in to 48in. Wright's also specialised in the supply of select stoves for the metal industries that included tinman's and lacquering stoves.

By 1883 Wright's stove business had grown in size, and trade was now conducted at two distinct locations. The making of gas stoves and other heating apparatus (and the sale on commission of gas engines) continued at the Broad Street works. The manufacture of castings for the gas stoves and apparatus was conducted under the name of the Argosy Fine Castings Co. at a foundry in Tennant Street, formerly in the ownership of May & Mountain, Engineers.

John Wright retired in about 1879, when he was approaching his sixtieth year. Sons George and John succeeded their father in the management of the company. Through

John Wright & Co. developed their range of gas cookers at the Broad Street works before moving to larger premises at Aston, July 1883. The Eureka cooker was one that helped to found the firm's fortune. *(Journal of Gas Lighting)*

their skills, trade continued to increase and soon outgrew the Broad Street site. The restricted space at Broad Street was given up during 1886, when the business was transferred to Aston and a larger site in Thimblemill Lane. Here both the foundry and stove works were accommodated on one site. These new works were provided with up-to-date equipment and had a railway siding that connected the London & North Western Railway, as well as access to the Birmingham Canal Navigations. Fresh capital was brought into the business when John Wright & Co. Ltd was formed, in July 1890. The first directors were Samuel Sanders (chairman of the rolled metal manufacturers, Charles Clifford & Son), Edwin Ludlow (chairman of Alldays & Onions Pneumatic Engineering Co. Ltd) and John E. Perry (a director of Brown, Bayley's Steel Works Ltd at Sheffield). The services of John Frederic Wright and George Ernest Wright were retained as joint managing directors.

During 1901 John Wright & Co. merged with the Eagle Range & Gas Stove Co. of Catherine Street, Aston. The Eagle Range Co. were first concerned with the manufacture of kitchen and other ranges, which were once common in Victorian and Edwardian households. The range was a foundry product assembled into a block of

different metal compartments that surrounded a coal fire. The heat from the fire was use to cook items in the various compartments distributed around the range.

The iron foundry had been constructed on land leased by George Gordon Brodie in 1884. Brodie and his partner, James Prior, traded as the Eagle Range & Foundry Co. The company was registered in September 1894 and in May 1899 changed its name to the Eagle Range & Gas Stove Co., when the adjacent business premises belonging to the Arden Hill & Co. Ltd was merged with Eagle Range. Arden Hill had made gas stoves at the Star Works, Constitution Hill, but had transferred their business to Aston and new premises located between Benjamin Mason's rolling mill and the Eagle Range foundry.

A year later another merger brought Eagle Range and John Wright together as one business. The Eagle Range foundry was enlarged to encompass the Arden Hill site and was extended along the canal side from Catherine Street to Portland Street.

The merger of Eagle Range and John Wright brought Harry James Yates into the concern as the new managing director. Yates was a progressive individual and was keen to introduce the most up-to-date scientific methods. Laboratories were built and research work in improving the appliances was begun. Paramount in their research was the aim to improve the lot of the housewife.

By 1914 John Wright & Co. was the leading member of an association of eight separate factories. All were responsible for the making of gas apparatus, but with the onset of war became devoted to government work. This included the manufacture of gas stoves, which proved essential to the making of munitions. The stoves served the Ministry of Munitions in various ways:

Heating of solid steel billets in making shell bodies.

Annealing and heat treatment processes in connection with the top of the shell body.

Drying the lacquer inside 15-in shells.

Heat treatment of copper bands.

Annealing of brass shell cases.

Heat treatment of shell cases returned from the war front.

Heating and mixing of chemicals used in explosives manufacture.

Tempering of springs.

Hardening of metals for tool making, etc.

John Wright & Co., furnace machine shop, 1917. The John Wright & Co. Essex Works at Thimblemill Lane occupied a strip of land sandwiched between railway lines and the Birmingham Canal Navigations. During the First World War production included a range of furnaces for munitions work. (Gas Journal)

Above, left: John Wright & Co., furnace machine shop, 1917. *(Gas Journal)*

Above, right: John Wright & Co., erecting shop for lip axis titling furnaces, 1917. *(Gas Journal)*

Left: John Wright & Co., crucible furnace erecting shop, 1917. *(Gas Journal)*

In June 1919 John Wright & Eagle Range became the leading member of a group of gas appliance makers that comprised the Radiation Group. The other two members were the Luton-based Davis Gas Stove Ltd and the Warrington-based Richmond Gas Stove & Meter Co. Ltd.

The works of John Wright came to cover an area of 20 acres that included land on both sides of the canal in Thimblemill Lane, plus another works between the railway and Holborn Hill. The Essex works were further enlarged with the completion, in 1928, of a new warehouse and distribution block that was located between the canal and Thimblemill Lane. Bridge connections were made across the canal to the existing part of the works.

Gas stoves in the semi-open style like muffles or the completely closed type proved a valuable asset to local industry as they offered a cleaner and more controlled form of heating. Birmingham Gas Department were keen to promote their use, particularly with the heat treatment of metals. During the 1920s sales of gas to industry started to decline. High gas prices were believed to be the cause, and some firms returned to coke-fired furnaces or adopted oil-fired ovens. Despite the drop in sales, the quantity of gas supplied to industry remained high. An important customer was the cycle industry, which used gas ovens for brazing, japanning and heat treatment of component parts. In tinplate work, gas was used for the soldering of kettles and saucepans. Gas ovens served many metal firms for purposes such as hardening and annealing.

John Wright & Sons (*Birmingham Gazette*, 1 April 1930)

One of the most fascinating spectacles in all the extensive works of Messr John Wright and Co. is to be seen in the gas cooker assembly shop. Down the enormous length of this shop travels an endless belt conveyor, three hundred feet long.

At one end of the conveyor basic components are placed – the cast iron framework of a stove – and so forth. And as the framework travels slowly along various things are done to it. Between the framework and the enamelled metal interior slag wool is packed: the doors are fitted and bedded in: and the connections and burners tested for leakages. Further along the conveyor the stoves are sprayed with the finishing coat of enamel: further along still burners are adjusted and the automatic heat controller is fitted on. And at the end of the conveyor the stoves are deposited to the despatching department packed ready for sending away.

The gas iron was another important product, which firms such as Parkinson & Cowan and John Wright supplied for domestic and industrial use. Heated flat irons had a long association with the laundry trade, and ironing stoves heated by gas proved to be a clean method of heating the irons. John Wright made flat irons at the Essex works in Broad Street, and later the Essex works in Thimblemill Lane. Flat iron design was improved during the twentieth century and John Wright had a range of ironing set models for domestic use.

Ironing sets generally comprised an iron (or a pair of irons), a heater and a trivet base. Some models had gas burners incorporated in the iron. The Beetall Manufacturing Co. produced both gas and box irons at their Victoria foundry in West Bromwich. Wright's also made the Mirror Gas Iron, which had a flexible connection to the burners that heated a polished, or nickel-plated, sole plate.

Gas irons and gas ironing sets continued to be made by the Radiation Group during the 1950s, when they were marketed under the 'New World' brand name. The New World range also included a gas poker that was used for lighting central heating coke fires. Gas irons proved difficult to convert to natural gas, and their manufacture generally ceased during the 1960s.

West Midlands industries were important suppliers to the gas industry, and provided items such as of pumps, retorts, pipes and a variety of brass foundry fittings. Gas engine makers were mentioned in *Birmingham's Industrial Heritage*. Their use became very important to the development of local industry, particularly the cycle and bedstead trades, which were both major users of the gas engine. In addition to T. Barker, Grice

The retort mouth-piece covered the mouth of the retort. Through the mouth-piece the charge of coal was inserted and the coke retracted. When carbonisation was under way the mouth-piece door remained firmly closed and gases from the retort were drawn through the pipe connection in the mouth-piece to the ascension pipes. *(Journal of Gas Lighting)*

Thomas Piggott were noted for structural iron and steel work, but were also gas and general engineers. Their factory was at Springhill on the bank of the Birmingham Canal, Winson Green Loop. In this 1930s view of Springhill a tram is seen making its way towards the canal bridge. Piggott's premises are seen on the right of the picture. *(Local Studies Department, Birmingham Reference Library)*

Brothers of Fazeley Street and Heath Mill Lane made gas engines for the local trades. Many gas engines were also provided by the firm of Crossley Brothers of Manchester. Delta Metals had a bank of Crossley gas engines that supplied power to their Dartmouth Street works up to the 1950s.

Many of these firms have all but gone. Radiation closed its Aston Works in the 1980s, but part of the firm survives in Aston. Radshape Ltd was founded in 1967 to shape and form domestic radiators. They expanded their business to include the supply of parts for the automotive sector and included Morgan and Rolls-Royce among their customers.

Thomas Piggott & Co. advertisement.

CHAPTER SIX

PAINTS & VARNISHES

Avariety of substances have been used to provide protective, and decorative, surfaces for brick, metal and wood. Colours, enamels, japans, lacquers, paints and varnishes all have a particular purpose as surface coatings. The origins of their use have been lost in the past, but commercial manufacture on an industrial scale is a much more recent event.

Varnishes were extensively produced in Birmingham and the surrounding district, where there was a large local consumption. Principal customers included makers of japan wares, iron bedsteads, brass foundry, bird cages and general wire work. In addition to the local market, Birmingham increasingly supplied colours and varnishes to the national market.

The manufacture of pure colours was another trade that developed with the varnish trade. Colours mixed with oils and varnishes produced a variety of paints, but were also of use to the dyer of cloths and wools. Local production of paints and varnishes continued to improve from 1900, despite the fact that most raw materials had to be imported. The rise of the cycle, engineering, lamp and motor industries had opened up a wide range of demands, where metal covering and protection was an essential part of the production process. These developments led to a wide application of enamelling and japanning in the area, and stimulated the making of gas and electric ovens by a select group of local companies during the twentieth century.

THE VARNISH AND LACQUER MAKERS

Varnishes are a mixture of resins in oil. They are essentially clear solutions, which are used for coating a surface and giving a gloss, and to defend the surface from the weather. Skill was needed to produce a useful varnish, and those employed in the trade kept their production methods and ingredients secret.

The basic components included natural gums that were melted at high temperatures and combined with hot linseed oil. After a process of further heating the mixture was thinned with turpentine to a consistency that could be applied with a paint brush. Other components were added to assist drying. These included sugar of lead, red lead, white copperas or zinc sulphate.

A variety of gums were used depending on the purpose of the varnish to be made. They included Gum Animi that was used in first-class varnishes, Gum Copal used in copal, polishing and oak varnishes and Gum Kauri (or Kowrie) that was the ingredient in many of the common classes of varnish. Other substances included Gum Mastic, Gum Damar, Gum Amber and Gum Dragon. Lacquers were a specific type of varnish that employed resins such as Seedlac, Shellac and Sticklac, which were common in Asia.

Varnish making was established in Birmingham during the eighteenth century. All component materials had to be imported, and were brought to the town by road wagon or canal boat. Purchases of the gums and oils were frequently made through a network of merchants, but sometimes cargoes arriving at one of the ports might be advertised for sale in a local paper.

The basic skills of the varnish and paint maker were essentially the mixing and heating of materials. Yet, there are many specialised aspects of the trade, as composition was varied to suit particular needs or functions. They included polishing, mixing and japanning varnishes. Colours could be added to the mixed varnish to form a type of paint. Other types of varnish were suited for application to a surface already coated with a dull colour or paint. Japan varnishes were applied and then heated, or stoved, to give a hard and protective finish. Names were given to differentiate the types and grades of varnish, and several firms added their own identification for the specialist versions that they made.

Selected List of Varnishes

The following is a list of some of the large range of varnishes whose composition was specially adapted to suit particular purposes.

Varnish Name	Use
Berlin Black	Stoves, ranges, fenders and edge tools
Black Tar Varnish	Buttons, hair pins, holloware, japanware makers and umbrellas
Brown Tar Varnish	Matchboxes, percusion cap boxes and tinware
Body Varnish	Coachmaking
Brunswick Black	Stove grate and ranges
Carriage Varnish	Coachmaking
Common Iron Black	General blacking work
Furniture & Oak Varnish	Furniture
Mastic Varnish	Used by picture mounters and artists
Paper Varnish	Paper hangers
Pontypool and Black Japan	Coach work
Quick Iron Black	Black iron bedstead laths, hinges and similar articles
Spirit Varnish	Paper-box and brass foundry
Willenhall Lock Varnish	Lock making and furnishing ironmongery

---

Varnish had a number of uses, but an important demand developed for the protection of woodwork, ranging from household furniture to stagecoaches. Application was a laborious process, as up to sixteen or eighteen coats might be laid down. The early development of varnish and lacquer in Birmingham was closely associated with the town's metal trades, and it seems that a number of manufacturers during the eighteenth century produced lacquers and japans not only for their own use, but also to supply out-workers. Little information has survived from these days, as the ingredients and process of manufacture were a jealously guarded secret.

An event which had considerable influence upon the development of Birmingham varnish trade occurred in 1740, when John Baskerville introduced the art of japanning into the country. The method involved the process of applying lacquer to metals, or other materials, and heating the object in a stove. It was similar to the method practised in Japan for several centuries. The business had developed in Birmingham to such an extent that by 1770 a dozen or so japanners (see page 92) were working in the town. To supply their needs, a number of varnish makers were also at work in Birmingham.

One of the first varnish makers was John Meredith, who set up in business in 1780 and later had premises between the Birmingham Canal and Lionel Street. Various members of the Meredith family came to have a share in the business, which became known as Meredith & Co. Business improved during the 1880s and they were able to open a second varnish works at 55–6 Ludgate Hill. Meredith & Co. transferred to a new purpose-built canal-side varnish factory in Western Road during 1890.

Samuel Thornley established a varnish factory beside Birmingham & Fazeley Canal, facing Lionel Street, in 1797. The original premises were at 5 and 6 Lionel Street and the works had wharf space near the bottom lock. On the opposite side of the canal were located Water Street rolling mills, which were the first mills in Birmingham to roll metal by steam power. The canal was also of use to Samuel Thornley, as it enabled the transport of both materials and coal to the site.

Coach varnishes and house painter varnishes were produced first. In 1803, Samuel Thornley went into partnership with his brothers-in-law, Thomas Knight and R. Sherratt, when the title of the firm was changed to Thornley & Knight. By 1803 the firm was also making a mixing varnish for painters. As demand increased a range of specialist varnishes was supplied. Cabinet and copal varnishes were produced and various oils such as linseed and shellac were kept in stock to supply painters' needs. Many of the new types were found out by trial and experiment, which was not without risk. Edward Thornley, the son of the founder, was killed in an accident at the factory. He was burned to death while making varnish in 1835. Despite the sad loss, Thornley & Knight continued to increase their range, and by 1861 produced sixty-four different types of varnish.

As orders increased the Lionel Street factory had difficulty meeting the demand. In 1875 additional premises were acquired in Alcester Street to cope with the amount of orders. The lease of the Lionel Street factory expired in 1902 and the decision was taken to relocate to a new site in Bordesley Green Road. The land taken by the company provided for future building extensions, as required. Some four generations of the Thornley family had been associated with the company by this date. In 1903 a limited company was formed with the third Samuel Thornley and his son S.K. Thornley appointed as joint managing directors.

Jeremiah Barrett established a varnish factory at 218–19 Bradford Street in about 1840 and was at one time in partnership with a Mr Hadfield. Barrett retired in 1864 and the business was taken over by Holden & Sanders in 1865. Arthur Holden had worked in the varnish trade and his experience proved essential to the management of the concern. From 1868 the business was carried on in his sole name. The firm specialised in black tar varnish for the japan trade and stoving blacks for Victorian slate mantelpieces.

During 1898 the company acquired land adjacent to Burbridge Road and Bordesley Green and eventually built a new factory there. The Bordesley Green works were fitted out during 1913 and equipped with the latest machinery for paint, enamel and varnish making and had extensive making and maturing rooms. Further improvements included a cellulose lacquer department, which was established during the 1920s.

The firm made many different types of varnishes. They included pale varnishes, stoving enamels (or japans) and specialist enamels. The special types of enamel comprised a long list of different titles such as Holden's stoving cycle enamels, bedstead enamels and finishes for the japan trade. There was also a dedicated black varnish shop for varnishes and copal.

It was common for Holdens to give specific names to a particular varnish, which was derived from the first customer who bought them; Pontypool varnish was a black stoving

Holden's Surface Coating Ltd, March 2000. The decorative façade of Holden's paint factory, Bordesley Green Street, includes descriptions of the products made by the firm. *(Ray Shill)*

japan for the slate mantle piece industry of Pontypool. This varnish created a texture of marble on various types of slate. Bradbury's was made for a firm of that name. Ashton's was produced for a Mr Ashton, a manufacturer of floor cloths. Nairn's was also made for a floor cloth manufacturer, which had special enamel in their name, while Taunton's was a coal black varnish for the Birmingham bedstead firm. Kenyon's varnish was manufactured for Entwhistle & Kenyon, a carpet sweeper manufacturer. Others include Hudson & Scott's copal and Barringer's copal.

A long-established Birmingham firm was Llewellyn Ryland, the foundations of which were laid by John Ryland, maker of brass and Britannia ware. He was assisted in the business by brother-in-law John Llewellyn. They acquired the lacquer business of William Lambley, of Caroline Street, and came to specialise in the varnish trade at premises located at the rear of 31 Newhall Street. When John Ryland died his son John Llewellyn Ryland carried on the business.

Gittings, Hills & Boothby had a varnish works and acid factory near Long Acre. They could trace their business back to the year 1773. Reade Brothers, who transferred their varnish and japan making business from Wolverhampton to Aston during the 1870s, established the Long Acre site. They set up the Tower Varnish Works beside the Birmingham & Fazeley Canal and with road access to Long Acre. They produced varnishes for coach painters, house painters and railway contractors. Stoving varnishes were also made for japanners, papier mâché and bedstead makers. A specialist product was a hard varnish for seats in churches and other public buildings. Hill Brothers took over the Tower Varnish Works and they subsequently merged with another local varnish maker, Gittings & Boothby of Park Lane.

Another varnish maker of repute was the firm of Docker Brothers. Frank Dudley Docker was born in Smethwick in 1862 and was the youngest son of Ralph Docker, a lawyer. He was educated at King Edward's Grammar School and trained for the law. He, and brothers Ludford and William, founded Docker Brothers, paint and varnish manufacturers, Deritend Varnish Works in Alcock Street, and later a second works on reclaimed canal land, which became the Birmingham Varnish Works in Rotten Park Street.

The art of varnish and lacquer making centred on special and secret recipes where the task was to combine the ingredients successfully. Many different combinations of oils and solids were required to suit the purposes of clients, and the skill of the workers included the ability to blend substances. The heart of every varnish factory was the mixing room, where the oils and ground powders were combined. Here a worker is seen in the mixing room at Docker Brothers, Rotton Park Street. *(Birmingham Art & Industry Magazine)*

Docker Brothers, main yard, Rotton Park Street. *(Birmingham Arts & Industry Magazine)*

Dockers supplied varnishes to the railway carriage industry, but also had business interests in the carriage and wagon building trade. They were instrumental in effecting a merger of several carriage makers that created the Metropolitan Amalgamated Railway & Carriage & Wagon Co. Ltd, that included the local firms Metropolitan Carriage & Wagon Co. Ltd, Saltley & Brown, and Marshalls Ltd of Adderley Park. Frank Docker was invited onto the board and eventually became chairman of the Metropolitan Carriage & Wagon Co. Ltd.

This close business arrangement ensured a ready market for the Birmingham Varnish Works products among the carriage and wagon builders in the Metropolitan Carriage Group, which included not only the Birmingham carriage works but also plants in Lancaster, Manchester, Oldbury and Wednesbury. Docker Brothers' head offices were transferred to Metropolitan Road, Saltley, where they were at the heart of the carriage building empire. The bulk of railway vehicles, at this period, had wooden bodies, and layers of paint and varnish were required for protection against the weather at home and abroad. A large market in railway vehicles existed across the world and the Metropolitan customers included railways in Africa, Asia, Australia, the sub-continent of India and South America. The range of colour schemes required was vast as each company had its own livery. At home the British railways comprised a number of independent companies with similar requirements. A vast array of private-owner wagons also ensured a steady demand for bright paints of different colours, and varnish.

The Metropolitan Carriage Co. merged with the railway vehicle building business owned by Cammel Laird during 1927. The new combine brought the Midland Carriage Works at Washwood Heath into the fold. The changes led to closure of some of the older plants and disposal of related properties. These were also changing times for Dockers' business. Steel-bodied railway vehicles were being produced in large numbers and traditional wood-bodied vehicle making was in decline. The demand for a varied range of varnishes had also lessened.

William Canning also made lacquers as part of a varied trade, which chiefly included the supply of electroplating plant and chemicals. W. Gunn, a general drysalter in Great Hampton Street, carried on the original business. W. Canning served an apprenticeship with Gunn and was later taken into partnership. The firm then traded under various titles; Gunn & Canning, Canning & Keating and finally W. Canning & Co.

The firm of W. Canning & Co. developed an interest in nickel plating in about 1883, and supplied nickel salts and anodes for nickel plating. During 1887 T.L. Hemmings & Co. patented a type of dynamo that generated electricity for electroplating. Cannings provided financial assistance for this work and enabled Hemming to found engineering works in Snow Hill, which were later taken over by Cannings. Thus Cannings became involved with the manufacture of electroplate dynamos. They also made motor generators, resistors and polishing lathes, in fact all the electrical side of electroplating. In about 1900 a chemical works was established in Bagot Street by Mr Round, manufacturing chemist. Control passed into the hands of Canning & Co., who made the Zonax brand of chemicals. A lacquer making department was commenced in about 1910.

Frederick Crane Chemical Co. had works at 22 and 23 Newhall Hill. They became known for the making of Zapon Enamel, which came onto the market in about 1890 and which was particularly suited for the brass trade. Zapon provided a colourless coating but also could be dyed any shade of gold, and in this form was used for imitation gilding of brass or electro-brassed ware. Cranes moved to new premises at Armoury Close, Bordesley and went on to produce a range of industrial finishes, which included lacquers, enamels, wood finishes and aluminium paint. They became an associate company of Imperial Chemical Industries, and Nobel Chemical Finishes of Slough traded from the same address. Nobel and Crane had a stand at the 1932 British

Industries Fair at Castle Bromwich, where they had on show various Crane products and a new range of finishes called Dulux. A couple of years later, Crane decided to vacate the Armoury Road site for new premises in Alma Street, Smethwick.

THE PAINT AND COLOUR MAKERS

Paints are another facet of the surface coating industry and comprise a vast range of different products, ranging from the inorganic paints such as lime-based whitewash to polymer vinyl coatings. Paints, like varnishes, afforded protection for materials against the weather. They comprised a solid material – the colour or pigment – which was finely ground and mixed with a liquid medium that assisted its application. This medium could be a number of things, including raw oil and in particular linseed oil or tung oil. The colours and oils were usually sold separately. A trade developed in the supply of colours, and several firms were established in Birmingham to supply colour to the painters. The colour manufacturers were aided by the invention of the Colour Mill, in 1835.

Certain types of paints and stoving varnishes were called enamels. The term enamel was a name first applied to glass-coated items, but it also came to mean a paint that gave a smooth, glossy surface.

During the 1820s chemical manufacture had been conducted at the Dartmouth Works, Ashted by the Badham family. With the death of John Badham the Ashted works were offered for sale during 1834. One William Badham became associated with Samuel Thornley (the varnish maker) to set up a colour works in Eyre Street. Thornley acquired a long strip of land between Eyre Street and a recently constructed basin of the Birmingham Canal Navigations and leased sections to different people. Badhams Colour Works was the first to be constructed, and appears to have been at work by 1835.

Badhams occupied the central strip of property through to about 1890, when they relocated to a new site in Rotten Park Street. Here their firm became associated with, or controlled by, Docker Brothers. William Badham made, or supplied, colours, paints and prussiate of potash. At least three different grades of white lead were produced: purest, superior (No. 1) and No. 2. Surviving invoices and bills reveal that the paints came in a variety of colours and names. Apart from a black, blue and yellow, there were Burnt Turkey, Venetian Red, Light Green, Middle Green, Deep Green, Vandyke Green, Burnt Senia, Lemon Chrome and Indian Red.

Painters prepared their paints by carefully grinding dry colours with linseed and other oils, such as those obtained from walnuts or poppies. The colours after grinding were usually kept in earthenware jars covered with a bladder skin that was tied down with waxed thread.

Thornley & Knight included paint in their sales ledgers from 1835, but varnish making comprised the bulk of their sales throughout the nineteenth century. By 1900 there was a growing demand for good quality ready-prepared paints for the house painter and coach builder. Paint grinding machinery was installed at the Bordesley Street works in 1905 and the sale of ready-mixed paints commenced.

During the First World War Thornley & Knight Ltd were chiefly occupied in making paints and varnishes for army vehicles, and special finishes for shells and armaments. Paints and varnishes were almost unobtainable for domestic use. The trade relied on Germany for the supply of essential colours, and the conflict also meant that import of raw materials such as linseed was almost cut off. Paint quality suffered, as substitute oils met with little success. After the war, production and quality reverted to normal, and within a few years new types of paint were being developed. The celluloid finish for motor cars came into production during 1925. Research also led to a range of synthetic varnishes and enamels. The synthetics heralded a range of new products, for

Thornley & Knight's factory, Bordesley Green Road, 1903. Varnish making in the Thornley family spanned three centuries. During the nineteenth century varnishes were made at factories in Lionel Street and Alcester Street. During 1902 a move was made to a new site in Bordesley Green Road, where both paints and varnishes were produced. The first part of the new factory was built alongside the corner of Cobham Road. *(Heartland Press Collection)*

The original Thornley & Knight premises in Bordesley Green Road, April 2000. *(Ray Shill)*

Coach builders' service section, Bordesley Green Road, Thornley & Knight Ltd. *(Heartland Press Collection)*

the sale of which distribution depots were opened in London, Liverpool, Manchester and Newcastle upon Tyne between 1925 and 1935.

Bombing during the Second World War heavily damaged the depots and the Bordesley Green Works. The varnish stores at Bordseley Green were particularly affected and were rebuilt after the war. By 1947 building extensions had come to occupy much of the land taken by the company in 1902. Production of enamels, paints and varnishes had continued to increase and the future of the company looked good. Samuel Kerr Thornley died in 1947 and was replaced by S.E.K. Thornley as head of the firm.

Bordesley Green Road is a long and straight road. It was, by the end of the nineteenth century, lined with brick works and marl pits. The land was subsequently reclaimed and adapted for factories. Three separate varnish and paint makers had factories in Bordesley Green Road: Asbestos Fireproof Paint, Arthur Holden and Thornley & Knight. The Thornley & Knight paint factory, rebuilt after wartime bombing, lines the left-hand side of the road. *(Archives Department, Birmingham Reference Library)*

The Titterton family were drysalters, oil, varnish and colour makers with business premises at 6 Snow Hill and a colour works beside the Digbeth Branch Canal, facing Dartmouth Street. John Tarratt Titterton, the head of the family, established the Ashted Colour Works during the 1830s and this remained in family ownership through to the mid-1860s. John, a native of Cheadle (Staffordshire), married Harriet Lane in 1828 at St Philip's Church in Birmingham. The sons succeeded to the business when John Titterton died, but it was Charles Richard Titterton who came to gain control of the firm. Charles then had a brief business partnership with William Hall, before setting up another varnish and paint works at 189 Park Lane, Aston. Hall retained the Dartmouth Street factory to make metal paints.

Jeremiah Barrett, varnish maker of Bradford Street, also set up a colour works, at 266 Bishop Street, in about 1863. When Barrett retired from the trade Bishop Street colour works became the property of the Birmingham Colour Co. They retained the, premises until about 1877 when the business was transferred to premises in Montgomery Street, adjacent to the Warwick & Birmingham Canal.

The making of colours was frequently conducted at chemical works, which made them as part of a larger range of substances. Notices for the sale of the original Lifford Chemical Works in 1843 mention colour mills and indigo machines alongside retort houses, lead vats and coppers. Further details of chemical manufacture are discussed in Chapter 8.

Many paint pigments were derived from mineral or vegetable sources, which imparted the required colour:

White:	antimony, barytes, chalk, china clay, lead oxide or carbonates, silica or zinc oxide
Yellow:	cadmium salts
Blue:	Prussian blue, cobalt salts
Green:	copperas, malachite

All paint components, as for varnishes, had to be brought to Birmingham. Apart from mineral and vegetable colours, another important ingredient was china clay, which was employed as binding agent and absorbent for oil and pigments. China clays were used in the secret process that made the colour ultramarine. Choice of paint colours was at first somewhat restricted, but with the development of the gas industry and the refining of certain by-products, a wider range became available. After distillation, coal tar produced a number of aniline dyes, considerably adding to the range of colours available to the painter, ink maker and dyer.

Some paint makers set up to produce mixtures of inorganic compounds for specific purposes. James Webster, who was later noted for refining aluminium at Solihull Lodge, experimented with metallic paints during the 1860s and was a partner in a metallic paint factory in Oozells Street, before his restless appetite for invention led him along another course. William Hall of the Ashted Works made paints principally used in the boiler, girder, gasometer, tank and railway wagon building trades. Hall used iron oxide which was ground finely in oil. The United Asbestos Co. Ltd produced a fireproof paint in which asbestos from their mines and factory at Turin, Italy, was ground down and used as the paint additive. A paint works was initially set up in Clement Street during the 1880s, but was later moved to St Vincent Street and finally Bordesley Green Road. For many years this branch of the United Asbestos operation traded as the Asbestos Fireproof and General Paint Co. J.N. Brown and T.D. Clare patented an anti-fouling paint in 1865 that included the mineral ilmenite, which was a titanium iron oxide ore. Llewellyn Ryland took up Brown and Clare's patent to make paints that included the ground oxide. A separate company, the Titanic Paint Co., was set up by Rylands to make and market this paint from their Haden Street Works.

Arthur Carr and William Carr established a paint, varnish and waterproof paper factory at Metropolitan Road, Saltley, which was set up in 1892. Known as the Saltley Bridge Works, the factory was one of several buildings, including tube and wire mills (Powers), located on a strip of land between the carriage works and the railway. The paint making side of the business was transferred to Artillery Street as Carrs Paints Ltd. The Artillery Street site occupied a strip of land between the Warwick & Birmingham Junction Canal and the Midland Railway and had originally been laid out during 1886 for the Birmingham Compressed Air Co. This ill-fated scheme had been set up to supply compressed air to drive machinery belonging to firms in the Digbeth and Deritend district. Its failure during the early 1890s led to the site being adapted for other purposes. When Carrs moved to Artillery Street, the property was shared with Batchelor & Co., scrap metal dealers and chemical manufacturers, which then specialised in recycling tin. Offers to lease the vacant land had been made in 1909, but it seems that was not until 1913 that the Carrs set up their factory. The Artillery Street Paint Works remained Carrs' head offices through to about 1970, when another move was made to the Westminster Works, West Heath.

Thomas Merry was another drysalter, who established a business in Swallow Street and Suffolk Street. He also engaged in the making of varnishes. When Meredith & Co. moved their varnish factory to Western Road, Merry took over Meredith's Varnish Works at 107 Lionel Street to make varnishes. During 1904 a second move was made, to larger premises at 157 Alcester Street, which he named the Westminster Works. Thornley & Knight had previously owned these premises, but had vacated them on the completion of their factory in Bordesley Green. The firm became Merry & Minton Ltd, and during 1924 another move was made to Alvechurch Road, West Heath, Northfield. The property at this time comprised a stamping and piecing works formerly owned by A.S. Cartwright. These works had been a First World War development on land adjacent to Edward Baker & Sons' black lead works. In peacetime Cartwright made toys, bells, children's reins and rattles. They had recently improved the site with the erection of two new factory buildings but had suffered financially, and debenture holders had appointed a receiver to sell the factory and plant. The site also included a rubber plant, run under the title of Kings Norton Rubber, which made seamless rubber goods such as bottle teats, valves and golf ball centres.

Cartwright's factory, known as the West Heath Works, was sold in June 1924, and by October 1924 Merry & Minton had made arrangements for the erection of another factory building between the existing structures.

Merry & Minton had a strategic situation. Placed close to the Austin Car Factory, they were in a beneficial position to supply the motor car works. They retained a separate existence through to the early 1960s, when their business was taken over by aircraft dope maker Cellon Ltd, of Kingston-upon-Thames. Cellon continued to make paint and varnish at the Westminster Works through to the late 1960s, when Carrs took over the factory.

Dockers' Varnish Works occupied a plot of land between Rotton Park Street and the Birmingham Canal. Docker Brothers was taken over by paint makers Pinchin Johnson in 1927, which later became a member of the combine International Paint. The decision was taken to enlarge the Rotton Park Works and extend production to a range of paints. Property was obtained nearby. Additional land was taken over from a former boat-building yard, occupied by Lovekins. Later, another important acquisition was the factory formerly occupied by McKechnie Brothers, which was relinquished by them after

The PPG group have taken over various properties and now occupy land on both sides of Rotton Park Street. *(Ray Shill 2000)*

Right: PPG group offices. *Birmingham Industrial Heritage*, page 85, reproduced an illustration of McKechnie Brothers' metal recycling plant. Part of this former factory has been retained by the PPG group in their Rotton Street Works. *(Ray Shill, 2000)*

Far right: Another part of the PPG factory occupies a corner of land that was formerly Lovekins boat building yard. *(Ray Shill 2000)*

a move to Aldridge. Rotton Park Works became known as the Ladywood Works and eventually occupied 8 acres. It became one of the major UK paint plants. Their surface coatings ranged from auto enamels to military paints. From 1976 a major part of the Ladywood site was the specialised Vehicle Finishes Division, which marketed six kinds of vehicle refinishing paints in a variety of colours. The Ladywood Works are now part of the PPG group, which continue to make paints for the automotive industry there.

On page 85 of *Birmingham's Industrial Heritage* is an illustration of the McKechnie Brothers' metal recycling plant. Part of this former factory has been retained by the PPG Group as part of their Rotton Street Works.

Llewellyn Ryland's business has been transformed over the years. They were varnish makers for a lengthy period. Just before the beginning of the twentieth century varnish making was moved from Newhall Street to premises in Baskerville Place, Broad Street, which had formerly been part of the Winfield's brass and bedstead factory. It was there that lacquers were produced incorporating a tradition, and presumably the skills, inherited from the firm of Robert Winfield. Varnish making was also conducted at Haden Street in a factory previously owned by John Player Heath & Co. Heath had set up the Haden Street Works during the 1850s, but had relinquished the property to Ryland in about 1863. A paint factory was set up in farm buildings adjacent to the original Haden Street Varnish Works. It was here that the Titanic Paint Co. made anti-fouling paints incorporating ground titanium ores, such as ilmenite. Llewellyn Ryland had interests in mines in Scandinavia and imported the ore into this country for processing.

In order to satisfy changing industrial needs Llewellyn Ryland adopted new product lines and abandonned old ones. Surface coatings production eventually replaced varnish making, and the company still trades from the Haden Street Works, producing colours for reinforced plastics. The transition from traditional paint making to pastes and flocoats is typical of the resilience of Birmingham industrialists, who have adapted to meet the needs of twenty-first century industry.

The Haden Street Works now produces polyester colour pastes, gelcoats and flocoats, mould preparation products and bonding pastes. They distribute these items worldwide, assisted by a sister company Llewellyn Ryland (China) Ltd, which is based at Tuen Mun, Hong Kong.

A Visit to Llewellyn Ryland, 10 December 2003

The firm of Llewellyn Ryland Ltd remains a prominent maker of colours for gel coatings and plastics. It has a long history in the trade that began with the making of varnishes, lacquers and paints. Early premises occupied in Newhall Street were vacated for larger premises in Haden Street, Balsall Heath.

In the 1950s the firm started making colours for gel coats and paste for the plastics industry and also devised a special PVC paint for the bedstead trade. They also made powder paints that were used in an electrically charged bath with anode and later cathode coating technologies. Their customers were varied and included Hoskins & Sewell of Bordesley, who used their products to coat hospital bedsteads. Another Birmingham manufacturer Kirby, Beard used Llewellyn Ryland lacquers for coating hairpins. Changes in demand for paints and varnishes have led Llewellyn Ryland into new markets. The lacquer factory in Baskerville Place was closed down and lost in the redevelopment around Centenary Square. The paint company was also disposed of.

The present Haden Street works are a modern factory, but the office block dates from the early years of the company. There are still two sides to the works. Behind the offices is the site of the original Varnish and Colour Works begun by John Player Heath and William Heath in the 1850s, but now used for mixing colours. Materials that arrive by road include polyester resin, which is now imported but had previously been supplied from a local company, BIP.

Entry into this part of the works is accompanied by the smells of the resins that pervade all parts. An important feature of this area is the rotary grinders used in preparing the ingredients for mixing. There is a garden in the centre of the works that separates the two sections, which is a haven of nature within an otherwise busy works. Passing by the garden, entrance is gained to the former paint works site. Here are storage areas, despatch and the mixing areas, where the all-important combination of colour and stability is achieved.

Located within is the mixing room; a host of colours are on view. Colours in liquid form are racked in barrels on the upper floor and these are fed down through pipes to different-sized mixing containers, where mechanical stirrers assist the blending to the paste or gel coat required. The rows of blending vessels are arranged in order and the process appears straightforward and simple. The appearance is, however, deceptive, as years of experience are drawn on to achieve the final product.

Current production has centred on the gel coats and pastes, which go to colour plastics. They also supply the ingredients used in marine paints, such as those used in covering fibre-glass boats.

W.G. Postans began as a varnish maker at 19 Lionel Street during 1843, when he took over a warehouse and factory buildings previously occupied by John & Edward Butler. They later became associated with Morley Brothers and transferred the business to premises at Trevor Street in Nechells. Morley Brothers were formerly located at Goodrick Street, but established the new works at Trevor Street in about 1908. Trevor Street was then a residential area, but the new varnish works were erected on a vacant strip of land, which extended back to Aston Church Road. Postans merged with Morley Brothers during 1909 and varnish production at their Lionel Street works was transferred to the Nechells works. Postans & Morley became known for the making of good quality and bright coloured enamel paints. The name of the firm finally reverted to Postans Ltd, and during the 1970s there was another change of address, to 95 Aston Church Road. Evode Powder Coatings acquired their business during the 1980s. Evode were adhesive makers based at The Common, Stafford. Postans was merged with neighbouring firm D. Worrall & Son Ltd in 1991 when the business decided to specialise in the manufacture of powder paints for everything from car parts to steel building frames.

Powder coatings also became the standard product of Croda Paints. Croda had taken over the Thornley & Knight Works in about 1977 and continued to occupy their Bordesley Green factory throughout the 1980s. The 1990s saw another move for Thornley's old business to Shaftmoor Lane. Birmingham's eastside had seen various industrial developments during the early twentieth century, which included a new railway carriage and wagon works and the car and commercial maker, Wolseley. Three paint makers had transferred production to Bordesley Green, but only one has remained.

Holden's had a long association with the paint trade, which can be traced back to their earliest days at Bradford Street. They continue to make surface coatings for the food canners at Bordesley Green and are now part of the ICI group.

Several other British paint makers had depots, warehouses and agents in Birmingham. C.A. Lines of 81 Albert Street was agent for J.B. Orr & Co., whose trademark was the Silicate Paint Co. that specialised in making exterior paints. Goodlass, Wall & Co. Ltd made paint at Liverpool and had depots in different parts of the country. Their Birmingham depot was in Great Hampton Street. Lewis Berger also had a depot at Tyburn Road.

PRODUCTS

ADVERTISING & SIGNS

Enamel coloured signs on a metal base were a product of the enamelled sign maker and the ticket writer. The signs were made for a variety of uses ranging from tram and bus stops, through street signs to metallic sign adverts for popular brands of soap, custard and cigarette. The smaller signs, which were the speciality of the ticket writer, were frequently made to fit shop windows. This trade was at its height during the late Victorian and Edwardian era (1880–1910), when demand led to several firms establishing in Birmingham. An essential part of the process was the use of stoving enamels and paints, which were applied to the sign surface. One such firm was the Birmingham Advertising Tablet Co. Ltd, which had the Sampson Works from 1896 until 1902. Their works fronted Sampson Road North and extended back to a basin beside the Warwick & Birmingham Canal. The premises included printing and varnish shops and a hydraulic press room that were located either side of a central area of stoves.

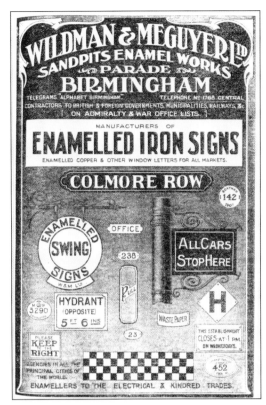

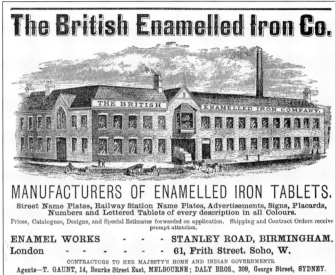

Birmingham had a small number of advertising sign makers who provided a wide range of colourful enamelled iron signs that ranged from business advertisements to bus and trams stops. Left: Wildman & Meguyver Ltd advertisement. *(Kelly's Directory, 1911)*; above: British Enamelled Iron Co. *(Kelly's Directory, 1884)*

CAR TRADE

With mass production in the car industry, the demand for particular types of paints was increased. Automobile bodywork required different finishes to suit the needs of private cars, commercial passenger vehicles, commercial trucks and wagons and trade vans, which were influenced by the materials used in construction, the conditions of production and, perhaps most importantly, cost.

By 1925 cellulose enamels had become almost universal for finishing private cars. Commercial passenger vehicles continued to be finished by traditional coach painting methods. Trade vans were often given undercoat paints and then were sent to the coach painter, who applied the required livery.

Car and commercial vehicle making has had an important influence on the paint trade. The invention of the spray gun enabled vehicle bodies to be covered at a faster rate, and also led to the development of paints best suited to its use. Modern car body painting has become a very technical process, with a series of steps including surface cleaning and laying down specialist coatings in a specific order for body shells and other parts. Certain paint manufacturers had to adapt their trade to supply a range of powder paints to meet customer demands.

COACH BUILDING

The timber employed in coach building mainly comprised English ash for the framework, mahogany for panelling, elm for planking, deal for flooring and American pine for roofing boards. English oak was used to make wheel spokes. The wood and iron components were coated with paint laid on to a considerable thickness. The doors and panels might receive up to fifteen coats. The first coats were white paint, followed by other colours selected for the vehicle. Six or more applications of copal varnish were then applied and afterwards polished.

JAPAN TRADE

Japan is a name given to a varnish or lacquer that is applied through heat. Japanning is an art that originated with the Japanese. The process consists of applying an opaque black varnish to the surface of the material to be japanned and baking it in a specially constructed oven. The Japanese made their varnish from the sap of certain trees, which after exposure to air caused it to develop a dark colour. Pulverised charcoal was added, and the varnish mixture was then applied and the coated object was baked in the oven. Several further layers were applied, and after each application the object was baked again. Once the final baking had been completed the surface was polished with a stone and water to produce a smooth, glossy finish.

The British japan-making trade used quite different materials than those used by the Japanese. Japan varnishes were composed chiefly of asphaltum, gum, linseed oil, turpentine, benzine and a colouring matter, such as charcoal or bone black. The purpose of japanning, as with all varnishes, was to protect the surface from corrosion or chemical action, but it also could be decorative, and the skill of application became the nature of the art. Japanning skills were particularly important to the development of the papier mâché trade, which developed in Birmingham during the eighteenth century and which will be discussed in detail in Chapter 10.

RAILWAY TRADE

Many workers moved from coach building to railway coachwork with the expansion of the railways and allied trades, which is why many early train carriages resemble stage coaches. Passenger and goods vehicles had bodies made of wood, which were covered in paints and varnishes to suit the livery of the customer.

TOY TRADE

Toy making was dependent upon paint and varnish manufacturers, as it consumed the widest range of finishes in large quantities. The British toy making industry saw rapid development after 1920, and paints were in particular demand as the trade needed attractive finishes to sell its products.

CHAPTER SEVEN

THE PLASTICS TRADE

Plastic is a term used to describe the ability to change shape and form. When a material or substance is said to be plastic the general meaning implies that it is flexible and capable of moulding into another form. During the twentieth century the word came into use to describe a growing number of materials formed from natural and synthetic compounds that could be shaped into solid and useful products. They were a mixed batch of substances derived from a host of different sources, but that when combined together formed a material that was moulded for a particular use. These new materials had varying degrees of structural strength, had the ability to retain their shape and could be coloured to suit customer need.

As scientists laboured with experimentation and formulation a new branch of science, the study of polymers, was born. Work was initially concentrated on a study of natural long chain molecules, such as cellulose and resins, and a greater understanding of their composition was gained. With time, people were able to produce synthetic polymers, and once this landmark discovery had been achieved the foundations of the modern plastics industry was established.

Although the plastics industry has its roots in the twentieth century, people have been used to forming finished articles from natural substances such as gutta-percha, india rubber and resin for a considerable time. The corporate inventiveness of Birmingham skill and manufacture frequently explored new uses and combinations of naturally occurring substances, and sometimes found commercial success. Davenport and Cole, Balsall Heath, used gutta-percha as a component in some of the imitation jewellery made at their Rea Works.

Ebonite was the first plastic material made by deliberate modification. This rigid, black material was obtained through heating natural rubber with sulphur. The first true plastic material is generally acknowledged to be Parkesine, which was made from pyroxyline and oil, producing a material form that could be made to imitate ivory, tortoise-shell, horn, hardwood, india rubber or gutta-percha. Credit for this invention was due to one man, Alexander Parkes, a Birmingham chemist.

Parkes was born in Birmingham. He was the son of a shopkeeper who lived near Edgbaston Street. Alexander was apprenticed to Thomas Messenger, brass founder in Broad Street. Here he learned the skills of the brass founder's art and it was those skills that Elkington & Mason chose to use when they later employed him as manager of the casting department. He had a fertile inventiveness and assisted Elkington's with early developments in electro-deposition. Parkes's contribution was the use of potassium cyanide in the process. With swelling confidence, Alexander Parkes embarked on patenting a number of diverse chemical and metallurgical processes, which included a method of extracting silver from lead, and tin from scrap tin plate. Another invention was a method for producing weldless tubes for copper and harder alloys. The Stephenson Tube Co. in Liverpool Street was formed to use the techniques in making tubes specially designed for engineering purposes and large diameter cylinders for calico printing. Parkes was manager of the Stephenson works, but the venture proved to be less successful, and the establishment was ultimately taken over by Messrs Everitts of the Kingston Works, Adderley Street. Parkes later devoted some his time to a new process of refining nickel from its ores, and together with Josiah Mason helped to set up a new refining plant at Birches Green, Erdington. These works, which were later carried on by Le Nickel, are mentioned in *Birmingham's Industrial Heritage.*

Parkes's skill and invention extended to several disciplines and many had commercial values. It was the experiments with collodion that would bear the greatest fruits. Collodion consisted of a mixture of pyroxylin dissolved in alcohol or ether. Pyroxylin was derived from cellulose nitrate (gun cotton), which itself was made through treating cellulose with nitric and sulphuric acids. Cellulose nitrate was highly flammable, and its varied uses were frequently prone to combustion. Cellulose was available from a number of recycled cotton sources, such as flax waste, rags and paper makers' half-stuff.

Pyroxylin was used as a constituent of varnishes and paints, but came to fulfil another purpose with the development of photography during the middle of the nineteenth century. Collodion was used a base material for photographic glass plates, but Parkes found that if castor or cotton seed oils were mixed with it, the material derived could be brought to varying degrees of hardness, and when mixed with certain substances and pigments resembled amber, tortoise-shell, malachite and ivory. Parkesine came to be made commercially in London, where the compound was then made up into knife handles, button cards, brush backs and napkin rings.

Parkes's first patent related to this plastic material was applied for while he was working for Elkington's in 1855. The patent mentions two new purposes for collodion and relates to processes devised while Parkes managed the new copper works at Burry Port, in South Wales. Parkes spent some five years there, living in a completely different environment from his native Birmingham. Burry Port was a coastal location which overlooked Carmarthen Bay. It seems that exposure to nature's harsher elements, wind and rain, in this district led Parkes to use his skills to find a waterproofing agent. The basic idea was the treatment of oils by action of sulphur of chloride, to produce an elastic solid, or adhesive compound and the use of gun cotton or similar compounds dissolved in naptha. The investigation also led Parkes to discover that he could produce a solid material for manufacturing purposes, and this formed the second part of the patent application.

He found that dissolving gun cotton in vegetable naptha, alcohol or ethers and mixing it with gums, resins or stearine produced a material that might be cast into shapes. Parkes returned to Birmingham and continued to develop the Parkesine process, along with other new projects. He left Elkington & Mason and by 1858 had set up as a manufacturing chemist in Bath Row, and was also proceeding with metal rolling experiments that were to become the foundation of the Stephenson Tube Works in Liverpool Street.

A second Parkesine-related patent was presented in May 1856, when a thick layer of collodion was formed into a solid sheet to support photographic film instead, or supplemental to, the glass plate then in use. Within seven years, Parkes was confident enough to exhibit Parkesine products at the 1862 International Exhibition in London and was awarded a bronze medal for his efforts. It was incentive enough to consider commercial production. Parkes devised machinery that dealt with the treatment of gun cotton and the product Parkesine. In 1865, patent no. 3,163 detailed several machines, which included a beating machine, a press and a centrifuge adapted to remove the nitrating acids used in the making of gun cotton. A particularly hard Parkesine was later developed. Parkes's patent of 1868 dealt with a method whereby Parkesine mixed in hot rolling or grinding apparatus with white starch, white flour and wheat or bleached cotton fibres produced a material that was moulded into billiard balls.

Commercial production of Parkesine ceased in about 1868, but the concept continued to be developed by other workers in both the USA and England. It was found that mixing cellulose nitrate with camphor could make another stable compound. American researchers called their product Celluloid, while the British workers named their product Xylonite.

The first synthetic plastics were also produced in America. Dr L.H. Baekland was a Belgian chemist who settled in the USA. He worked on the phenol-formaldehyde reaction at his own laboratory in Yonkers, New York. This work began in 1902 and with a careful study spanning several years he developed a process which led to the making of a synthetic resin that Baekland named Bakelite. The first US patents were taken out in 1907.

The inception of the UK operation was in 1904 as the Fireproof Celluloid Syndicate Ltd. They produced a hard lacquer called Damard, which provided a useful protection for brass and other metals. This was marketed under the Damard Lacquer Co. During 1910 the business of the Fireproof Celluloid Syndicate was incorporated into a new company called the Damard Lacquer Co. Ltd. They set up business at cramped premises at 98 Bradford Street, Birmingham. The lacquer mixing section was located on the second floor of the building.

There was considerable sales resistance to the new Damard Lacquer in the British brass industry, which preferred to use a hot lacquer known as shellac. Damard was applied cold and then the article was 'stoved' in an oven. The most important market was in the United States, where businessmen were more receptive of the new technique. Local manufactures did eventually take up Damard Lacquer and it was found to be particularly useful in the brass bedstead trade. Seeking new markets, the company also began to diversify into resin production.

An aerial view of the Bakelite Factory, Tyseley. *(Heartland Press Collection)*

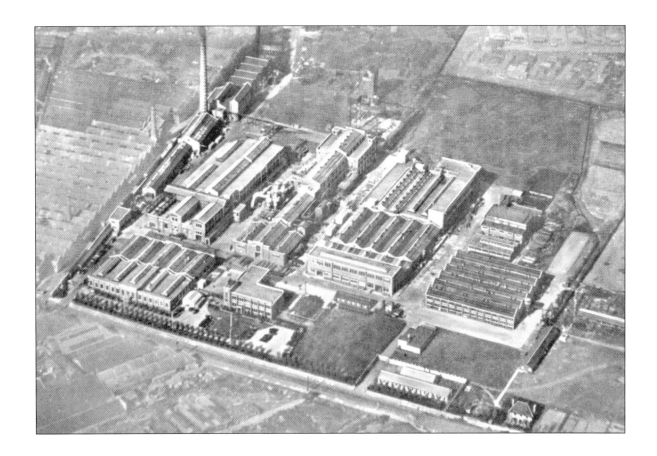

Resin manufacture at the Bakelite Works, Tyseley. *(Heartland Press Collection)*

During the First World War the demand for plastics increased and in particular there was a new market with the Admiralty, which required plastic materials to sheath electric cables. The demands of war production led the Damard Co. to take new premises at Cowley, Middlesex. In 1921, Damard established another factory at Greet, where they made resin and varnish. Among their products was Bakelite resin. By 1924 the worst of the depression was over and wireless manufacture was rapidly becoming an important trade. This led to increased demand for Bakelite in all its forms. The building of the Greet factory provided a ready supply of Bakelite resin for several local firms, who installed moulding machines to work the resin into various products.

Meanwhile Dr Baekland had extended his Bakelite production into the UK, forming Bakelite Ltd in 1921. Various British company acquisitions were made in December 1926, including Damard, which was brought into the Bakelite fold. Bakelite Ltd also took over the Ideal Manufacturing Co. of Sparkbrook in March 1929. During 1928 plans were made to concentrate production at Tyseley and plans for a new plant were formulated. The first part of the Tyseley plant was opened in 1930.

Machines that shaped plastic had their origins in the metal trade, but new methods and machines were devised to improve production. The machines that shaped plastics involved two basic methods. The first usually incorporated the heating of the material and shaping through moulding and extrusion. The second involved the setting of the material in a mould or die to form the required shape.

Several methods of moulding were developed, and Birmingham firms employed three versions. The oldest technique was compression moulding, where the material was heated in a mould and then pressed into shape by a hydraulic press. Modern plastic production tends to employ injection moulding. This process first consisted of heating plastic granules until they were sufficiently fluid. The fluid mixture was then injected into a relatively cold mould, where the plastic solidified and took on the shape of the mould.

Extrusion moulding machines replaced the earlier compression type of machine. Here an extrusion machine is seen making plastic whistle parts at Hudson's Whistles, Barr Street. *(Hudson's Whistles)*

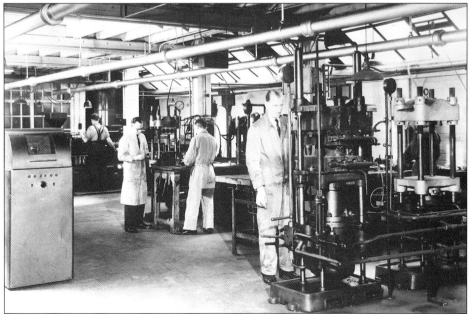

When the plastics industry came to Birmingham, machines of the compression moulding type were used. Here a compression moulding machine is seen in use at Hudson's Whistles, Barr Street. *(Hudson's Whistles)*

A third method was rotational moulding. Here, finely ground plastic powder was charged into a hollow mould. The mould was then closed and rotated in a large oven. The plastic material melted and coated the inside surface of the mould. The mould was then removed from the oven and allowed to cool. Rotation was continued for a period afterwards, and then the mould was opened to extract the moulding. Other methods of plastic production included blow moulding (for plastic bottle manufacture), calendering (for sheet production) and vacuum forming (for making chocolate box linings).

Early pioneers in the use of Bakelite moulding techniques were GEC and Lucas. Bakelite moulding insulation work was carried out at GEC in moulding shops near the River Tame, facing Tame Road. Bakelite powder usually sold to the electrical trade consists of a Bakelite resin combined with wood flour, or canvas flakes, and other fillers and colouring matter. At the Witton Moulded Insulation Works, the earliest Bakelite mouldings were produced by gas heating, but this method proved unsuitable for accurate control of moulding temperature. It was decided to use steam heating. Hydraulic presses were installed to form the shapes required. Early presses were of the hand-operated single action type, where the mould was charged, or filled, on a bench and placed in the press for each operation. The press was closed and heat applied for a suitable period; the press was then opened and the mould removed in its closed condition and dismantled on the bench. Semi-automatic presses came to be used, by which the process was speeded up. With these presses the mould was kept in the machine. The press opened the mould, and the operator put a charge of Bakelite into the mould. The press was then closed and left for a specific period and on being opened again ejected the finished moulding. In this method the operator was not required to handle the mould in any way.

GEC established its Witton Moulded Insulation Works in 1916, originally to meet the needs of the electrical industry for plastic components. These needs were extremely varied, embracing, in the course of time, a host of insulating components, industrial and domestic electrical accessories, valve bases, radio cabinets, telephone handsets and so on. A wide range of plant was provided that was capable of moulding, and finishing and assembling the mouldings.

The Witton Moulding Works expanded production to include electrical and general engineering, automobile products, toys and games; household appliances, tableware, furniture; clocks, toilet goods and photographic goods. Rationalisation within GEC led to the transfer of the moulding department to the former Rectifying Works, in Deykins Avenue. GEC established the Mercury Arc Rectifying Works at Witton during 1937, which became the first plant in the world devoted to the making of this type of rectifier.

The works were taken over by Linpac, where heavy plastic mouldings for the automotive industry were made. A visit made to these works in August 2000 found a number of large presses in use to turn out mouldings for car bumpers. These were automatic extrusion machines, with a robot element. Each machine was fitted with a heavy steel tool that comprised the moulding surface. Plastic granules were fed in through a hopper at one end and complete mouldings produced at the other. The process was continuous, the robot arm opening and closing the mould at regular intervals. Moulding and trimming took place inside the machine, the only human intervention being to remove the plastic waste and scrap.

The establishment of Bakelite resin manufacture in Birmingham encouraged commercial moulding ventures around the city to supply firms who chose not to invest in plastic moulding. Frederick W. Evans was one who saw the potential of the new trade and set up in business making plastic mouldings at a factory in Long Acre, Aston in about 1930. He formed F.W. Evans Ltd in May 1932 and carried out Bakelite moulding on a site sandwiched between Hockley Brook and Long Acre. During 1936 plans were submitted

A description of the Bakelite Moulding Department, Lucas Works, Formans Road
(Lucas Reflections, 1934)

Stopping at a large contraption the guide explained:

This is a 100 ton machine moulding press. You will notice that the punch is fixed to the head or top of the press and there are 36 impressions, that is there are 36 small punches all the same, forming as it were a multiple punch. There are two sets of dies, each corresponding to the multiple punch and which slide on rails from the front of the press underneath the punch to the rear of the press. The object of this construction is to enable one set of dies to be unloaded and refilled with Bakelite powder while the other set of dies engages with the punches and 'cures' or moulds the powder. By this method by a system of hot water under pressure – a recent innovation which ensures even heating, a very important feature in bakelite moulding.

The moulds themselves are very impressive. They are Chromium plated, which ensures greater durability, and imparts the highest polish to the moulded article. Their intricate and very forms shining as only chrome finish can shine, these tools present a truly remarkable spectacle. In wonderment, you ask, 'And who makes these tools for you?' and of course, the guide, who has been waiting for this, tries in an unassuming way to say. 'Oh, we make them all ourselves, would you care to see our tool room?'

But just a moment, let us watch this press work; the press has just closed; the press operator winds the handle on the extreme left of the press and 36 mouldings spring out of the die. He then threads a metal comb under the moulding and winds the handle back again, leaving 36 mouldings on the comb. These are removed in one operation and emptied into the work-box. Then with a jet of compressed air he blows any swarf or 'flash' as it is called and commences to load the die with metal inserts and Bakelite powder. This time, however, the Bakelite is in the form of tablets, and this is a more convenient and expeditious way of introducing the correct weight of material in each die cavity. The operator then opens the press and winds another handle which takes a die with the newly-cured mouldings to the back of the press and brings the freshly loaded die into position under the punch. The press is then closed again and the operator proceeds to remove the mouldings and reload the die with inserts and Bakelite, and so repeats the cycle as before.

for a new plastics works on the site. The new plant was built and equipped the firm with a base to progress in the industry. The firm remained family controlled, on the same site, through to the late 1980s. A range of Bakelite and modern plastic extrusion products was manufactured there. Another supplier of plastics was the Birmingham Mica Co. Ltd, South Road, Hockley. This firm began as a mica merchant and went on to make mica insulators for the electrical industry. Plastic moulding became a lucrative earner for the firm during the 1930s.

Elliotts were associated with the making of plastic goods and precursors such as Galalith and Erinoid. Edwin Elliott founded the firm of E. Elliott at 55 Frederick Street to import and manufacture imitation precious stones and merchandise for the jewellery and fancy goods trade in 1910. From 1912 he was also associated with the British Optical Lens Co.

The Frederick Street factory was developed as a machine shop for the manufacture of vegetable ivory goods such as studs and bushes for the electrical trades. Elliotts also had the agency for Galalith, a material made from the milk protein, casein, which was used for the manufacture of knife handles and buttons. Supplies of Galalith were imported from Germany, but these were lost during the First World War and it was replaced by another plastic type material, Erinoid, which was made in England by Erinoid Ltd.

In 1916 the company moved to Warstone Lane, bringing the optical and fancy goods sides of the business together in the enlarged premises. During the 1920s the firm decided to commence Bakelite moulding at the Warstone Lane Works and installed presses to make a wider range of items, such as radio parts.

Elliott's works, Cheapside. Edwin Elliott was a pioneer in the Birmingham plastics trade, manufacturing a range of products at factories in Summer Lane and Cheapside. *(Local Studies Department, Birmingham Reference Library)*

Many established Birmingham firms suffered during the depression of the 1920s, but new trades such as the plastics industry were more fortunate. By 1927 Elliott's business outgrew the Warstone Lane factory and it moved to larger premises in Brearley Street, and transferred again to the nearby Victoria Works in Summer Lane where techniques and machinery were updated to keep pace with the demands of the industry. Compression moulding machines were used at first, but these were later replaced by injection moulding machines. Both Bakelite and synthetic plastic products came to be made.

On 23 May 1936 Edwin Elliott Ltd was formed to amalgamate the optical lens and plastic business under one company. The additional finance created through the issuing of shares enabled the company to open a new plastics moulding works at Cheapside, Birmingham in about 1937. A new factory was also commissioned in 1938 in Bescot Crescent, Walsall. Enemy action destroyed much of the Summer Lane Works during the war, and plastic production was then concentrated at the Bescot Works.

The supply of a new range of polymers, such as vinyl, for plastics was developed in America, and this became the mainstay of modern plastic production. Jarrett, Rainsford & Laughton introduced plastic products as part of their range after G.A. Laughton visited America in 1936. Laughton met Abe Goodman from the firm of H. Goodman & Son, New York, who made hair curlers and other hair accessories. Goodman was already making curlers in plastic by injection moulding, and Laughton was quick to appreciate the advantages of this material for his own products. Abe Goodman came across to Birmingham a few weeks later and Twinco was formed, with capital supplied equally from Goodman and Jarrett, Rainsford & Laughton.

Malcolm Laughton was sent to the Goodman factory in Leominster, Massachusetts, to learn about the injection moulding business. Injection-moulding machines were then installed at the Birmingham factory and production was commenced towards the end of 1937. The first major product was vinyl acetate combs that were made using a two-impression die. Other products included a hair slide. Tenite (imported from America) was also used as a moulding material.

Jarrett, Rainsford & Laughton had premises in Kent Street and Lower Essex Street. The Globe Works, Bromsgrove Street, were purchased in 1939 to meet the anticipated demand for plastic products. These premises had previously been occupied by the mirror manufactory of O.C. Hawkes, mentioned in *Birmingham's Industrial Heritage*. The Globe Works provided much-needed work space, but repair and alterations were needed before the premises could be used for plastic moulding. Only a third of the building had been converted when bombing destroyed the whole premises.

The whistle maker, Hudson of Hockley, was among the local firms to install moulding machines for the making of plastic whistles. They have also been described in *Birmingham's Industrial Heritage*. Several firms installed moulding machines for the motor trade. Perhaps the most innovative were the rotational moulding works which were operated by Linpac at Long Acre during the 1990s. They produced large hollow mouldings and were particularly noted for the supply of litterbins and grit bins to local councils and several railway stations in the West Midlands.

Another aspect of the plastics trade was laminate manufacture. The firm of Tufnol in Perry Barr is named after the laminated product that is still made in Birmingham. They were established as a subsidiary of George Ellison Ltd, switchgear makers, and began as the firm called Ellison Insulations Ltd. Laminates were first made as electric insulators for use in the switchgear factory, but then came to have much wider applications.

Impregnating layers of paper or cloth with a resin was the basic process for laminate production. Variable numbers of these layers were then stacked together in a press and heated under pressure to cure the resin and seal the components into a solid and rigid mass. The resin was supplied in different forms that included lumps, solutions, varnishes and cements. The base came in the form of specially selected paper, canvas or asbestos. Ellison spent years developing the product before setting up a new company. Once the process was perfected, a new factory was built in Wellhead Lane, opposite the Ellison factory. It opened for production during 1930.

Although laminates were usually made from a paper base, this process involved building up layers of treated paper, canvas, cambric or asbestos to make a product of great mechanical strength. Tufnol was sold as sheets, tubes or rods and it was possible to fashion Tufnol products into mechanical parts such as pinions for gears. Blanks for the production of pinions and gears were cut from heavy sheet fabric Tufnol up to 3in thick. Fabric gears were unaffected by water or oil and avoided corrosion. They were also noted for their hard-wearing capabilities.

Another product was the key, or wedge, used in the railway industry. The Tufnol 'key' and pad was used as an insulator in cases where the track comprised steel rails and steel sleepers. The rail rested on a thin Tufnol pad and Tufnol keys were driven in at the side of the rail to hold it in place. Standard sheets of Tufnol had a brown colour and the base was varied according to use. Tufnol used for electric insulation had a special paper made from either wood or cotton. Where a degree of heat resistance was needed, asbestos was used. Other Tufnol products used fabrics ranging from fine cambric to heavy duck cloths.

The making of Tufnol used both heat and pressure to form the final product. The first stage of manufacture involved impregnation of the paper or fabric with a spirit solution containing a dissolved resin, and specially designed machines. The material was then passed through steam heating and drying chambers. From here the fabric and paper went on to be formed into different shapes. The making of sheet Tufnol required cutting of the treated material to a specific size and layers of this material were built up to a stack of specified thickness. The stack was then loaded between steam-heated platens on a hydraulic press. The heat softened the resin and expelled the air as the mass was compressed. Then after a period of sustained heat and pressure, the resin component hardened to form a unified mass. The sheets taken from the press were then trimmed to remove ragged edges and passed to the warehouse ready for sale.

Tufnol Ltd, Perry Barr. There is still a market for the laminate materials produced by this factory. *(Ray Shill, 2005)*

Tubes of Tufnol were made by feeding rolls of treated paper onto a machine with several electric heated rollers, which wrapped and compressed the paper onto a steel mandrel. Layers of treated material were built up to the required thickness and trimmed before the material-covered mandrel was transferred to a heavy steel mould and pressed between hot plates. The pressed tubes carried excess resin and paper, which was trimmed off with a saw. The tubes were then ground and polished before the mandrel was removed. All shapes of tubing, rods and solid bars were made. Many were to specialist designs that included a square bore and round exterior for making carbon brush holders, and tubes with round a bore and hexagonal exterior for making nuts for use with Tufnol bolts.

Located in a separate part of the Tufnol factory was the machine shop, where solid blocks of Tufnol were shaped and cut. Connections for high-tension work were made here, where copper conductors were embedded in a Tufnol base.

Yet another aspect of the plastic trade was extrusion, which was the method used for covering cable and wire. There is little evidence that plastic extrusion was carried out by Birmingham firms, who preferred to engage in moulding. There remain in the city a number of moulding firms, as well as several mould and tool makers. Among their number are Barkley Plastics, Highgate, which make a range of injection mouldings for the automotive and aerospace industries, and include camping equipment and battery boxes for Yuasa among their product range. There is also an engineering department on site, which is equipped with CAD and CNC machines for the shaping of the metal tools and moulds.

CHAPTER EIGHT

THE CHEMICAL TRADE

ACID MANUFACTURE

In 1746 Roebuck, a Birmingham doctor, set up in Steelhouse Lane, Birmingham, the first factory in the world to use lead chambers for condensing sulphuric acid and reduced the price of acid from 40s to 2s 6d per pound. The acid was already in demand for treatment of metals, and demand increased as the Birmingham metal trade developed. Several sulphuric acid manufacturers were established in the Birmingham and the Black Country during the nineteenth century. Local canals were often used for cheap transport of material such as pyrites, which formed the basic supply of sulphur for acid production. Another essential ingredient was the nitrogen oxides derived from nitric acid or potassium nitrate.

A second useful acid for metal treatment was muriatic, or hydrochloric acid, which was a solution of hydrogen chloride gas in water. Hydrogen chloride was a by-product of alkali making, which used common salt (sodium chloride) to make sodium carbonate. The salt industry of Cheshire, Staffordshire and Worcestershire provided a class of salt known as Broad Salt, whose quality was unsuitable for domestic consumption, but ideally suited for chemical manufacture.

Sulphuric acid was also known as oil of vitriol, the word vitriol meaning 'sulphate'. This acid was made at the Steelhouse Lane works through to the mid-1820s. Samuel Garbett assisted Roebuck in commercial manufacture of the acid, and it was Garbett who came to control the Birmingham plant. Samuel Garbett was an enthusiastic supporter of inland navigation and became a proprietor of the Birmingham Canal Navigations.

Garbett eventually gave up his chemical works in favour of James Alston and James Armitage, who had charge of oil of vitriol and aquafortis (weak nitric acid) manufacture there during the first decade of the nineteenth century. It was a relatively short partnership, as James Armitage left to set up another works near Aston Road that extended back to the Digbeth Branch Canal. James Alston & Son continued the works, now numbered as 17 Steelhouse Lane, through to the mid-1840s. They also made colours for the paint makers at Old Brasshouse Yard, Coleshill Street. Armitage & Son continued to make acid at the Aston plant until about 1881.

Birmingham chemist Richard Peyton was another early pioneer in the manufacture of vitriol. Trade directories as early as 1808 record Richard Peyton as a chemist and vitriol and aquafortis manufacturer in Holt Street. The Peytons were a non-conformist family, long settled at Cattespool, near Tardebigge, Worcestershire. Richard Peyton set up the chemical works and brought his son, Abel Peyton, into the firm to assist him, and it was Abel Peyton and his sons who carried on the business when Richard Peyton died. During Abel Peyton's control an extensive works was established beside the Digbeth Branch Canal. These works, which fronted Lister Street and Oxygen Street, gained great benefit from the canal link for the transport of raw materials.

Abel Peyton had other business interests, which included the railways. He was a member of the provisional committee responsible for the construction of the

Birmingham & Derby Junction Railway and became a director of that company and its successor, the Midland Railway Co. Abel's sons followed diverse occupations, ranging from the bedstead trade, as discussed in Chapter 4, to continuing the family chemical business.

Nineteenth-century trade directories list several makers of sulphuric acid in Birmingham. Among their number was William Shorthouse. He established a canal-side chemical works in Shadwell Street for the making of vitriol and aquafortis. Shorthouse began as a varnish maker in New Market Street, but added the plant at 65 Shadwell Street during the 1850s.

Principal acid makers were located in the Black Country. Among their number were the firm of Chance Brothers (Oldbury) and William Hunt (Wednesbury) who combined in 1898 to form Chance & Hunt Ltd. They also took over 65 Shadwell Street, which became their stores in Birmingham. Chance & Hunt vacated these premises about 1911 and Peyton & Son chose to move their chemical plant here from Oxygen Street. Peyton remained owners of the Shadwell Street Works until 1965, when the firm were taken over by Albright & Wilson.

In 1822 John Sturge began business in Bewdley making dyers' solutions for the Kidderminster carpet trade. Various other chemical preparations, such as citric acid, were subsequently added to the list. In 1831 John Sturge decided to move his works to Birmingham, where a new factory was established beside Wheeleys Lane. Edmund Sturge then joined the firm and the business was carried on as Sturge Brothers. They principally engaged in the manufacture of citric acid, tartaric acid and potassium bicarbonate. In 1841 precipitated chalk was added to the list.

Sales of citric acid increased. It was made at a new factory located at Selly Oak from 1833 to 1844, Wheeley's Lane and later Lifford. Supplies of the acid were obtained by refining imported lime and lemon juice. The limes were grown in the West Indies and from 1852 the company became associated, in particular, with plantations on the island of Montserrat.

Birmingham and district had several factories for the production of acid and other chemicals. The Selly Oak Chemical Works, beside the Worcester & Birmingham Canal, was begun for this purpose but subsequently adapted to make phosphorus for matches. Arthur Albright was instrumental in the change and was involved in the management of the works until production was moved to Oldbury. *(Heartland Press Collection)*

ARTIFICIAL MANURE

Chemical works and distilleries refined by-products of the gas industry to produce a range of many other useful products. Several refineries were located in the Black Country, where the network of canals provided the primary means for the transport of the cyanogen, gas water and tars made at the gas works. Gas water was enriched with ammonium salts and this by-product was commonly used to make the artificial manure, ammonium sulphate. The Nechells Chemical Works were established in Cattells Grove to refine the by-products from the local gas works. Brotherton & Co. Ltd acquired these works in 1898. They received ammonium liquor (gas water) by pipeline from the three main Birmingham works, Nechells, Saltley and Windsor Street, and refined the impure liquid to extract pure ammonium sulphate (sold as fertiliser) and pure liquid ammonia. Spent oxide was also purchased from the gas works to extract the sulphur to make sulphuric acid.

Brothertons also had chemical works at Bromborough (Cheshire) and Leeds. Coal carbonisation began to decline from 1950 when rationalisation in the gas industry, as noted in Chapter 5, brought other means of gas production into use and also progressively substituted natural gas for coal gas. Chemical refining of the by-products declined with the programme of gas works closures. Nechells Chemical Works closed with the cessation of carbonisation at the main Birmingham works.

Sturge Brothers came to Birmingham and set up chemical works at Wheeley's Lane, where products such as citric acid were once manufactured. The demand for pure calcium carbonate encouraged the building of a new factory at Lifford to deal with the supply of this commodity. In this aerial view the original factory beside the canal drawbridge is seen. *(Heartland Press Collection)*

Sulphates were also obtained as a by-product of phosphorus making. Local phosphorus maker Albright & Wilson of Oldbury sent regular consignments of sulphate from Oldbury to Hickling's Chemical Works in Andover Street for conversion and refining into manure.

CALCIUM CARBONATE

Arthur Albright, brother-in-law to Edmund Sturge, joined the firm of Sturge Brothers in 1840. Arthur was instrumental in the establishment of the Selly Oak works to make phosphorus, potassium chlorate, pure sulphur and sulphuric acid. Albright left in 1855 to found a new plant at Oldbury. Edmund Sturge later sold the Sturge business to Charles and Frederick Clayton, and they in turn sold the business to John Wilson in 1887. The residual calcium chloride had been sent from Albright & Wilson's Oldbury factory by canal barge to Sturge's Wheeley's Lane plant. There it was treated with soda ash and carbon dioxide in absorber barrels to produce precipitated calcium carbonate (PCC).

In 1898 Albright & Wilson moved phosphorus and potassium chlorate production to Niagara in America to take advantage of cheap hydroelectric power. Carbon dioxide had been collected from processing of the solid residue obtained from wine barrels, which was used to produce sodium and potassium tartrate, cream of tartar and tartaric acid and this gas was used to make potassium bicarbonate. Later the main source of carbon dioxide for the company for both bicarbonate and PCC was the imported lime and lemon juice mixed with chalk in the manufacture of citric acid. Once calcium carbonate supplies from Oldbury ceased the company decided to invest in a new limestone kiln at a new site. The Lifford Lane site was purchased cheaply and was well placed for canal transport alongside the Stratford-upon-Avon Canal.

CHARCOAL PRODUCTION

Charcoal was required for iron and steel making, and charcoal burners once produced large quantities from British forest wood to supply these trades. A purer form of charcoal was an ingredient of the black japan lacquers. J. Singleton supplied a range of fine chemical products. In 1838 Singleton took over a piece of property facing Eyre Street, where he established a chemical works. Among the products made here were purified charcoal and acetic acid. Spring Hill Basin, which joined the old main line of the Birmingham Canal, served the works.

PHOSPHORUS MAKING &
VESTA MATCH MANUFACTURE

Arthur Albright became a partner in the firm of Sturge Brothers on the death of John Sturge in 1840. Albright was keen to adopt the manufacture of phosphorus, which was needed for the manufacture of the Lucifer, or Vesta, match. At this time phosphorus was extracted chiefly from phosphates found in animal bones. Bones and acids needed for the process were brought to the works by canal boat. Albright took over the Selly Oak citric acid works and converted them for phosphorus making. He left the company in 1854 to found a new phosphorus works at Oldbury, where supplies of strong acid were readily obtainable.

Working with certain forms of phosphorus had a drastic side-effect, commonly referred to as the phosphorus disease. Phosphorus was initially available as yellow phosphorus and it was this form that was used to make the Vesta, or Lucifer, match.

The price of one box of matches was ½*d*; but the price of all the matches used in England could not recompense the stunting and dwarfing, the premature death of children and the early death of men, whose demise had been preceded by years of lingering torture – the flesh rotting off their bones and the bones crumbling beneath the flesh. Many suffered from a condition known as 'phossy jaw'. The human cost in match manufacture was high, and the sufferings endured by the match workers eventually became a matter of public concern. It was suggested that by making proper rules and regulations and enforcing compliance with them, a great deal of suffering to both children and adults might be averted, and indeed the conditions of match making was one of many cases that influenced the passing of the Factory Acts Extension, 1864.

David de Bermingham's match factory in Thomas Street, Aston, made wax vestas by hand, and almost all the staff employed there were girls. The process started with the manufacture of wax tapers, which were made in a long room by young women and girls. At one end of this room some of the workers were employed to dip one end of the taper in a phosphorus mixture. Dipped matches were then removed to the drying room, which was kept hot by air circulating from stoves. In another room boys were employed using steam-driven machinery to make match boxes. Nearby were the packing rooms, where girls put the matches in the boxes.

George Dowler had another match factory, in Great Charles Street, where match making was conducted in premises adjacent to his brass foundry. Here phosphorus dipping was conducted in the drying room. Generations of the Dowler family had been associated with casting fancy brass articles, including letter balances, but match making was a new business set up by George Dowler during the 1850s. Dowler transferred his match making to the Plume Works, Aston, during the mid-1860s, where he was also engaged in the production of ammunition cartridges. Here business was carried on for only a few years before the works were sold and match making ceased.

At Lodner's, in Hill Street, matches were dipped in sulphur and the phosphorus mixture in a garret at the top of building, open to the roof, with ladder steps communication between floors. It was a scene typified by Charles Dickens in his many books. Children were often forced to work in these conditions to add to the family income. In one case a father stopped his child on the way home from work, took money from him and spent it on drink. Hillier's, Lichfield Street, was another small-scale operation, where work was done in an upstairs room.

William Kohler, a native of Würtemburg, also made lucifer matches in Birmingham. In Germany the government appointed inspectors. Works people disliked the match manufactories and so they contracted for labour from prisoners. The match works were better designed, they were well ventilated, and clean linen and exercise in the open air were considered preventatives for contracting phosphorus disease.

De Bermingham and Dowler were considered the two principal match makers in the town of Birmingham. At de Bermingham's works some 32 miles of cotton were daily made up into vestas or wax matches. Cotton passed through a solution of melted wax and stearine and was converted into a continuous wax taper. After the wax had cooled, the cotton was cut into lengths. The end was dipped in a molten chemical composition, of which phosphorus formed the chief ingredient. Match boxes were of two types. One version was small or round, made of pasteboard and covered with a glazed chequered paper, each box containing about 60 vestas; the other was a tin box containing 250. The tins were cut out by machinery and turned to the required shape, after which they were japanned, all processes carried out at de Bermingham's manufactory.

A new type of phosphorus, known as red or amorphous phosphorus, became available during the 1850s. Red phosphorus did not readily catch fire and had a higher combustion temperature compared with the yellow type. It was therefore much safer and, more importantly, had fewer of the dangerous side-effects common with the yellow form. There was a disadvantage, however. Match makers had to mix the red phosphorus with potassium chlorate to create a mixture that would ignite. Birmingham match makers declined to adopt the red phosphorus, and paid the ultimate price once safety legislation took hold.

Arthur Albright led the way for red phosphorus making when he adopted a new process devised by Professor Anton Schroetter, of Vienna, Austria (1849). During 1851 Albright took the Schroetter process and applied for a British patent to manufacture amorphous phosphorus, which was granted in January 1852. Albright's method converted yellow phosphorus through heating in cast iron vessels. He believed his method of amorphous phosphorus production averted the evils of the Lucifer match trade, and during the 1870s demand for his product among the match makers increased. The Birmingham match makers went out of business at about the same time!

PHOTOGRAPHIC PLATES

The early use of collodion as a component of Parkesine has already been mentioned. Collodion was also an important ingredient in making photographic plates. Richard Norris, a doctor of medicine and professor of physiology at Queen's College, Birmingham, was an enthusiastic photographer. He was credited with the development of the first dry collodion plate during the 1860s and in about 1894 brought out a new version of dry plate. Norris was involved with a company set up to produce the new plate at his home in Yardley Fields Road, known as the Birmingham Dry Collodion Plate Film Co., but which shortened the title to the Birmingham Collodion Plate Co. a few years later. Norris had difficulty obtaining sufficient quantities of pure alcohol at a cost-effective price. The business was wound up, but Norris continued to live at Yardley Fields Road, where his residence became known as the Laboratory.

Another local company was originally known as the Birmingham Photographic Co. They were both photographers and manufacturers of photographic paper. They moved their business in about 1901 from the Criterion Works, Great Charles Street to new premises at Albert Road, Stechford. The company changed their name during 1914 to become the Criterion Plates, Papers & Films Ltd, and remained at this location until about 1970. They were latterly known as Criterion Graphic Products Ltd.

SOAP MANUFACTURE

A popular type of soap was made and sold as solid bars, commonly known as hard soap. Birmingham people obtained supplies of hard soap from both local sources and other long-established works in Bristol, Liverpool, London and Warrington. Improvements in transport routes through canals and railways and early advertising in newspapers and periodicals stimulated new markets and led to certain firms gaining an important share of the trade.

Several West Midlands soap makers were established beside the canal network, and these included works in Smethwick and Tipton. Birmingham also had a few soap makers. Three types of hard soap were manufactured:

White soap, made from soda and tallow.
Mottled soap, made from soda, tallow, kitchen grease and sometimes palm oil and coconut oil.
Brown soap, made from soda, palm oil and resin.

Boiling oil and tallow, or a mixture of oil, tallow, resin and caustic soda, was part of the process for the manufacture of hard soap. The solution of these different compounds was called lee. The first step was to dissolve sodium carbonate in water through boiling and then siphon off the carbonate solution into another vat to be mixed with caustic lime, where the heating and boiling were continued for another hour. The clear lee was pumped into another container, or reservoir, and allowed to cool. The pans used to make soap comprised large cylinders of wrought iron up to 20ft in diameter and 15ft in depth, surrounded by coils that conveyed steam for heating purposes. Tallow and lee were then added into the pans and heated. Tallow was readily available from abattoirs and was refined from fat cut from cattle and sheep carcasses. In addition to soap manufacture, tallow was also required for candle making. The combination of tallow and soda led to a reaction known as saponification. Common salt was then added, which made the tallow rise to the surface. The spent lee, which contained glycerine (from the tallow), sodium carbonate and sodium chloride, was then removed. Further lee was added and the process was repeated until all the tallow was converted into soap. Boiling was continued to evaporate as much of the liquid content as possible. The steam was shut off and the soap was allowed to cool again and settle for a period of some twenty-four hours. The remaining lee separated from the soap and the soap was removed by ladle and poured into a 'lift'. The lift was a series of wooden or iron moulds secured together to form an open vat. The soap mixture was then stirred with a crutch, which gave the soap a smooth and uniform appearance. Then the soap was left in the frame for about a week to harden. The hardened soap was extracted from the frame and divided into bars by a cutting machine. The final product was packed and sold as white soap.

Hard soap was not the only product made, as varying the ingredients enabled a range of others such as Primrose, Extra Pale, Tallow Crown, Palm Oil and mottled soaps to be made. Primrose Soap was produced through the addition of fine resin to the tallow mix. Palm Oil bleached by nitric acid was another ingredient mixed with tallow to make a variety of Crown and mottled soaps.

In 1834 the Birmingham Patent Soap Co. was formed to investigate the possibility of making soap with mica to add an abrasive quality and to take up Mr Hewit's patent on the process. It was intended to use mica from the waste obtained from the china clay industry. A legal dispute that developed between the shareholders appears to have delayed the project progressing, but the basic idea may have been adopted at the Farndon Gossage soap factory, at Stoke Works, Worcestershire.

Birmingham soap makers were few in number, but among them were George Smithson and John Pickering. George Smithson was a wholesale grocer who had premises in Smallbrook Street. A small soap works for the making of mottled soap was established during the 1880s in St Jude's Passage (off Hill Street) and to the rear of St Jude's Church. His son, John Snowden Smithson, had charge of this works for some ten years until about 1894, when soap making ceased. John Pickering began as a tallow chandler and merchant in Pershore Street. He arranged for the building of the Rea Soap Works, 64 Bissell Street, during the mid-1880s to make hard soap. John Pickering died in 1900, but both the soap works and the retail outlet were continued by the firm of John Pickering & Son Ltd until about 1926, when the soap works were sold to Hackwoods Soap Co. Ltd. Hackwoods produced soaps, such as the brand Jack Tar, there until the mid-1950s.

Another type of soap was borax. Arthur Robottom established the borax soap trade in Birmingham. He visited the borate lands of southern California during 1873 and decided to set up a works to make borax soap powder (Robottom's Pure Californian Borax) at 34 Ludgate Hill during 1874. These works were taken over by the Borax Co. Ltd and production increased. The business was moved to larger premises at Newmarket Street during 1876. The firm did not prosper, and during 1878 went into voluntary liquidation. Jesse Ascough, of Handsworth, purchased all rights, including patents, and set up a new firm, the Patent Borax Co., to run the business. Working conditions at Newmarket Street were grim. The premises were conversions of tenement houses in a slum district. A small workforce worked in clouds of biting dust generated by the grinding mill. The sieving was done in the open and the men worked with noses and mouths muffled.

A second move was made, to larger premises in Ledsam Street, during 1893. At the same time the Patent Borax Co. became a limited company and the injection of capital enabled fresh investment. New machinery was provided for grinding the borate salt into powder. During 1908 packing machines were installed to replace the old method of hand packing. The Ledsam Street works abutted the canal and there was a basin which went into the works. Coal and soda ash were brought in by boat and borax soap powder was sent out by boat. Production of borax soap was further increased from 1919, when another plant at Tipton went into production.

SURGICAL DRESSING MANUFACTURE

Southall Brothers formed on 31 December 1897 to take over the premises of Southall Brothers & Barclay and T., W. & W. Southall. The firm were wholesale chemists and druggists at Lower Priory, Birmingham; pharmaceutical and analytical chemists in Bull Street; manufacturers and dealers in chemical apparatus in Broad Street; and manufacturing chemists, drug grinders, makers of surgical dressings and sanitary appliances and distilled table water at Dalton Street. The company also made cod liver oil at Balstad in Norway.

Four acres of land was acquired in 1897 at Ward End, where the new company erected mills and laboratories. The mills were later taken over by Smith & Nephew, and are now run by Accantia on a considerably reduced scale. Current production is confined to sanitary towels.

Above: The original Southall Brothers & Barclay factory fronted Alum Rock Road and still forms part of the factory complex. A change of ownership brought the Ward End site into the Smith & Nephew fold, but by the time this picture was taken a management buy-out had led to the sale of the factory to Accantia. *(Ray Shill, December 1999)*

Southall Brothers & Barclay set up a factory at Ward End for the manufacture of chemical and sanitary products. Various factory extensions were made to the rear, including a now demolished block in Woodland Road. *(Ray Shill, December 1999)*

CHAPTER NINE

BEER & LIQUOR ENGINE MAKERS

The town and later the city of Birmingham had a number of breweries that brewed ale, beer and porter for sale or supply to the beer shops, public houses and inns around the town. There was also an extensive trade in retail brewing where publicans and inn holders brewed on their premises exclusively for their customers. A market developed for the supply of equipment and fittings for the premises that sold beers, cider and liquor.

Sale of ale, beer and porter was originally conducted direct from the barrel, but during the nineteenth century mechanical devices were developed using pumps and plumbing skills to deliver beer and other liquids, such as wine and cider, for sale. The term beer engine refers to the hand-pull device that raised beer from the cask in the cellar, or elsewhere, to the serving area of the beer shop or public house. The whole was an assembly of wood and metal. A solid wooden top and case made from mahogany, walnut or oak formed the basis of the structure, to which the hand-pull mechanism was affixed. Makers were skilled carpenters and plumbers who fashioned the complete system for delivering beer from the cask to the customer.

The origins of the trade date back to the end of the eighteenth century and Joseph Bramah's patent of 1797, which dealt with clarifying and drawing off malt liquors. Two more patents in 1798, granted to Thomas Stratton and William Hart, specifically mentioned machines capable of raising ale, beer and wine from cellars and other low places.

Birmingham's link with the metal trades enabled a number of beer engine makers to be established in the town. The arrangement included cast brass cylinders, metal rods and taps. Pewter, an alloy of tin and lead, was a common metal component, although mandol silver might also be used. Beer engine makers were therefore pewterers, but they were also plumbers when they came to install systems on site. Makers included the firms of Masons and also Yates, but the best known firm was Gaskell & Chambers, who still provide bar fittings, although they are longer based in Birmingham.

Bar fittings were supplied by manufacturers who had the engineering skills to make brass, pewter and other components; specific mention of dedicated beer engine makers appears later. Bimingham trade directories published in the 1820s list Joseph Harper (84 Bromsgrove Street) as a beer engine maker and also mention John Wilkes as a plumber, glazier and painter at 85 Lichfield Street. Wilkes went on to expand his trade to include brass foundry, beer engines and garden engines, and moved to larger premises at 61 Stafford Street during the 1830s, when competitors in the beer engine trade included James Cook (47 Holloway Head), William Harper (104 Suffolk Street) and Joseph Stevens (64 Price Street).

The Yates family, who could trace their pewterer's trade back to 1797, established a beer engine factory at 40–2 Coleshill Street under the partnership of Yates & Birch

YATES AND BIRCH,
PEWTER AND BRASS WORKS,
39 & 40, COLESHILL STREET, BIRMINGHAM,

Manufacturers of Beer Machines, Liquor Fountains & Recesses, Ale and Wine Measures, and all kinds of Pewter Goods, Lift Pumps, Brass Cocks, Garden Engines and Syringes, Pan and Sanitary Water Closets.

Sole Manufacturers of Farmer's Patent Self-acting Water Closet, Stokes's Registered Hydraulic High Pressure Tap, and the Patent Ombrosome or Portable Shower Bath.

Wholesale Depot for Carson's Salting Instruments.

Yates & Birch advertisement, 1854.

during the 1840s. Other 1840s traders included S. Harrison & Co., beer engine makers and cider motion makers at 52 Park Street, and Thomas Mills of 71 Bromsgrove Street.

Samuel Mason set up in business making beer engines at the Britannia Works, 56 Dale End during the 1860s. He quickly established a reputation for quality and won medals for beer engines and spirit fountains. William Perks Jnr set up another works at 50–2 Dale End, where his patent engines were produced.

Wilkes's factory in Stafford Street changed hand a couple of times, passing to J. Morgan & Co. and later to Peter Gaskell. The firm of Gaskell, Chambers & Foulkes, who traded as engineering brass founders and copper smiths, came into being through the merger of two separate businesses. Cornelius Chambers had come to Birmingham in 1884 as a junior partner to John Merritt, brass founder, of 13 Great Charles Street and assisted Merritt to build up a trade in the supply of beer engine fittings. This partnership

Gaskell, Chambers & Foulkes advertisement, 1898.

GASKELL'S
PRIZE
Beer Engines & Bar Fittings.

Patentees and Sole Makers of the

"MERRITT" CORKDRAWER,
"SWIFT" ,,
"SAFETY" ,,

And every Hotel Requisite.

GASKELL, CHAMBERS & FOULKES, Ltd.,
Dale End Works, Birmingham.

was dissolved during the early 1890s, when Chambers bought Peter Gaskell's business in Stafford Street, at the same time laying the foundations of an important bar fitting empire. Chambers acquired Perks's former factory at Dale End. Perks's business had been taken over by Joseph Newey & Co., but during 1894 was passed on again, to Gaskell & Chambers. Further changes followed in 1897 when Gaskell & Chambers became incorporated as a public concern. They amalgamated with the rival firm of Yates & Greenwood of Coleshill Street in 1902, and built up an extensive trade that specialised in catering supplies and bar fittings.

Samuel Mason continued to compete with Gaskell & Chambers until bankruptcy in 1910. Gaskell & Chambers then purchased Mason's bar fitting trade, but these events did not prevent the restarting of the Mason trade under the name of Harry Mason Ltd at 55 Dale End from April 1910.

Cornelius Chambers was a Black Country man, born in Kingswinford, whose first chosen profession was the law. In 1883 he married Ada Addenbrooke, whose family were long established in the coal and iron trades. A strong supporter of the Conservative party, Cornelius became Sir Cornelius Chambers in 1933, as reward for his long-term political and public services. He continued to run the firm, steering it through the depression years of the 1920s and 1930s. Both the Dale End and Coleshill Street factories were modernised and extensively enlarged during this time and they also had a separate wood store at 8 Coleshill Street. At the onset of the Second World War their factories were converted for war use, making fuses and other work. Cornelius Chambers died in August 1941. He was replaced by his two sons as joint managing directors.

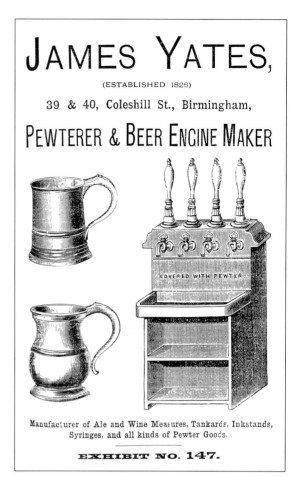

JAMES YATES,

(ESTABLISHED 1826)

39 & 40, Coleshill St., Birmingham,

PEWTERER & BEER ENGINE MAKER

COVERED WITH PEWTER

Manufacturer of Ale and Wine Measures, Tankards, Inkstands, Syringes, and all kinds of Pewter Goods.

EXHIBIT NO. 147.

Yates advertisement, 1886.

Enemy bombing caused damage to both Gaskell & Chambers factories, as well as destroying all their records. Extensions to the Coleshill Street premises were made during 1936 and 1937, including a section alongside Market Street that became known as the Cabinet Works. Here the company specialised in carpentry skills, producing all the wooden fittings for bars. There were setting out rooms, saw mills, joiners' department, polishing shops and even a separate beer engine department. The Dale End factory extended along Masshouse Lane and occupied a square of land and contained offices, workshops, a coppersmiths' department, brass foundry, pewterers' and polishing departments. A new factory, known as the Dalex Works, was completed in Coleshill Street during 1947 and 1948 when the machine shop, foundry, polishing and pewter departments were transferred from Dale End. Further extensions to the Dalex Works were made during 1955, when new buildings were erected to the rear and alongside Doe Street.

The postwar bar fitting trade proved to be a very lucrative one for the firm. It had depots in different parts of the company and some out-based manufacturing facilities, but much work was still continued at Dale End and Dalex. This included fine pewter work, cabinet making, a foundry department and the beer engine and cellar fitting department. Cabinet work was a particularly successful earner as demand for fitted bars for licensed and other premises such as coffee bars, milk bars and other catering outlets provided much new work.

The supply of bar fittings required an extensive fleet of road vehicles. Gaskell & Chambers' fleet is seen here in about 1955. *(Gaskell & Chambers Magazine)*

Below, left and right: Gaskell & Chambers had a large engineering department at the Dalex Works where the various components required for the making of beer engines and bar fittings were produced. *(Gaskell & Chambers Magazine)*

Gaskell & Chambers' company affairs were reconstructed at the end of 1961 and a holding company was set up in January 1962. The reorganised company grouped the various depots together as regional areas, renaming some districts in the process. Improved status was given to certain subsidiary companies such as the Non Drip Measure Co., which was based at Croydon.

The year 1963 was an important time of change for the firm. The death of the chairman, John A. Chambers, in May 1963 marked the end of control by the sons of Cornelius Chambers. His place was taken by Martin Chambers, retaining family control for a third generation. The year 1963 also marked the closure of the Cabinet Works in Coleshill Street. The land was needed for the new road developments by Birmingham Corporation. Cabinet work was transferred to a factory at Highlands Road, Shirley. Dale End works had effectively ceased to have any manufacturing facilities several years before.

Engineering for the group now centred on the Dalex Works, Coleshill Street, but this aspect was also to be moved to Drayton Road, Shirley. The new group headquarters and engineering works were opened in May 1967 and became the Dalex Works. The original works in Coleshill Street were vacated and Gaskell & Chambers' link with the centre of Birmingham ended. Other developments included the development of the factories at Thornton Heath. These had been formerly Redwing, light plane makers. Gaskell & Chambers moved their Croydon Works there to continue the manufacture of measures.

CHAPTER TEN

PAPER MAKING

Paper making in nineteenth-century Britain was conducted at various mills across the country. Many of those mills working during the first part of the nineteenth century were water powered, but these later gave way to steam-powered mills.

The ingredients that went into the paper came not from wood pulp, as they do today, but from recycling old cloth, ropes and rags. There were seven processes: sorting the rags, cutting the rags and other materials, dusting the rags, boiling, tearing or maccerating, paper making by hand or machine, and paper cutting.

In the first five processes women and girls were chiefly employed, in the last two, men, youths and boys. Rags were cut on open tables. Females of all ages were employed to cut and sort rags or cotton waste. The tables had a hole in them in which an upturned knife was set, over which the female cutter drew the rags. The rags were often dusted by steam power, chopped by machinery and afterwards boiled in huge iron vats. Various procedures were then adopted that included grinding by rag engines, bleaching, steeping, drying and beating to make pulp that became paper. Where paper was made by hand, workers were grouped in teams of three per vat. Two of the three were adults. The first adult was the vatman, who dipped his mould or frame into the vat of pulp. The second adult was known as the coucher, who received the mould from the vatman and turned out the sheet of paper from the mould onto a felt or blanket. The third person was an apprentice of sixteen or seventeen years of age, known as the layer. His duty was to take the sheets one by one after they came from the press, separate them from the felts and return the felts to the coucher.

Paper mills came up for sale from time to time and sometimes auction advertisements provided information about the working of the mill. Following John Gould's bankruptcy, Littleton and Harvington paper mills on the River Avon were offered for sale in March 1804. Littleton Mill was said to contain two vats and vat houses, with leaded stuff chests, three dryers, two solls, one finishing room, one rag room and two storerooms. Harvington Mill had been recently erected to make unfinished paper called packs. This mill had the right of water and a main wheel that was shared with the adjoining corn mill, worked by Edmund Smith. Harvington paper mill contained an 'engine', *stuff chest* and one *vat hog* and pot. There was also a patent hydraulic press, which evidently was used to compress paper pulp. Harvington Mill had a reputation for the making of hand-made paper throughout the eighteenth century and supplied major towns, such as Birmingham and Coventry, and had consequently built up a regular supply chain for rags.

Birmingham paper merchants used the products of the mills dotted around the Midlands, often using the canal and navigable river networks to bring the paper to their warehouses in the town. Canal carrier Robert Samuel Skey founded his canal carrying business on profits from the paper trade, when he inherited the paper merchant business from his father-in-law, John Brown. Local water-powered paper mills were few in number. Those that existed were often adapted from mills built for other purposes such as the milling of corn or the working of metal. They included Aston Furnace, Witton, which had been used to smelt iron until about 1782, but had been let for other purposes. Paper was made there during the 1820s and 1830s. The last recorded paper makers there were Grafton, Mole & Barrow, and once they gave up the trade Aston Furnace was adopted as a wire mill.

Manual production of paper came to be superseded by steam-driven mills where paper pulp was flattened between large metal rollers. Birmingham Paper Makers produced various types of paper, but their most common range was brown paper used in bag making. Fine paper production was generally not a Birmingham speciality. One of the factors that prevented the making of fine paper in Birmingham was the general impurity of the water.

Birmingham had a select group of steam-powered mills which came into existence during the nineteenth century for the manufacture of common brown paper and paper bags. Mill owners included James Baldwin, who was in the partnership Baldwin & Vale, engravers, copper platers, letter press makers, printers and paper dealers in Newhall Street, but then added brown paper making to his business lines during the 1830s. He made paper in Sherborne Street and later at the Kings Norton Paper Mills, which were located beside the Worcester & Birmingham Canal near Lifford. Another manufacturer was John Inshaw, who established the Aston Manor Paper Mill in Chester Road. John Inshaw was a respected engineer, whose inventions earned him certain notoriety. His latest venture was the manufacture of rough brown paper, for which there was a regular demand to make paper bags and wrapping paper.

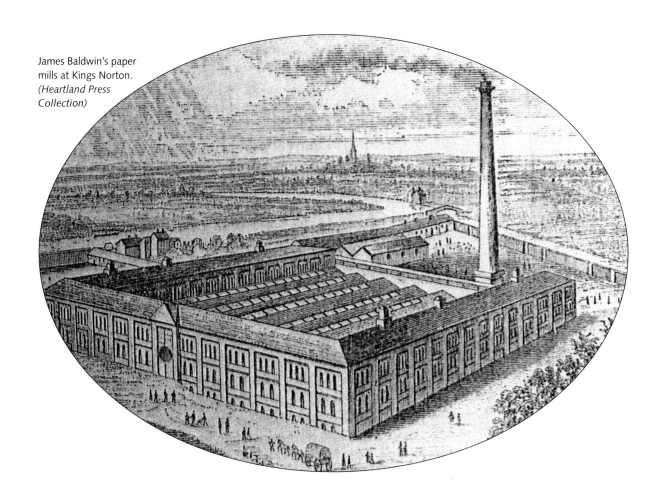

James Baldwin's paper mills at Kings Norton. *(Heartland Press Collection)*

A Description of Aston Manor Paper Mills, Cheston Road
(*Birmingham Daily Post*, 6 December 1875)

Proceeding up the gateway, the boiler house first attracts attention. It is tenanted by twin boilers, constructed on an improved plan. Viewing matters in order of detail, one passes into the department where ropes and sacking are cut up prior to being boiled down. The cutting machine and 'rag boiler' are driven by a separate portable engine of 8 hp. The material, after it is chopped, passes into a large rotary boiler, where it undergoes the action of the steam proceeding from the boiler, which turns the chopping engine. It is then placed into a large rag engine, which is driven by a 60 hp compound steam engine designed by Mr Inshaw. The crude mass passes from the rag room into the machine room, the machinery of which is driven by a 10 hp engine. It then finds its way in chests, or cisterns, after which it finds its way into the feeding cistern and flows down in pipes to the 'knotter boxes'. The next process is that the pulpy mass is delivered onto moving wire gauze that delivers it to rolls covered with felt. It then passes through a pair of iron rolls and is raised up to a number of drying cylinders, where it is subjected to different degrees of heat. Before it is ready for reeling the paper has to pass through a series of calender rolls. A number of rolls of paper are then placed upon cutting machines where the paper is cut to the required sizes. The cutting machine is driven by a 4 hp steam engine that also drives a hydraulic press under which the paper is placed before being made into packages.

A duty was imposed on paper, which had the effect of restricting the quantity made. Shortly after this duty was repealed, three local businessmen founded a new paper mill in Birmingham in 1862. They were Thomas Bird Smith, John Benjamin Stone and Frederick Knight, but only Thomas Smith had any practical experience of the paper making trade. He had worked for his uncle, James Baldwin, who owned the Kings Norton Paper Mills. Smith, Stone & Knight's first paper mill was located beside the Birmingham & Warwick Junction Canal in Landor Street. There was initially one paper making machine and mill, but a second and larger mill was added. The company purchased a vacant site on the corner of Mount Street and Cranemore Street, in 1873, where the Grove, or Birmingham Paper Mill, was built. A private limited company was formed on 10 March 1894 to assist the firm gain additional capital and to finance the new paper bag factory, which came into operation during 1895 at Landor Street. Further expansion followed when Smith, Stone & Knight purchased the Aston Manor Paper Mills, which previously belonged to Inshaw, in 1899.

Rags and old rope continued to provide the raw material for local paper making throughout the nineteenth century. Birmingham had some five or six independent rag merchants who gathered material from a variety of sources. Rag pickers were employed by the firm to sort and grade rags for beating and pulping by steam-driven engines. In fact, steam engines remained the popular choice for rag treatment even when gas engines had been adopted by other paper makers. In 1906 a new steam engine was installed to power the Aston Mill.

Waste paper was slowly adopted as an alternative source to rags. A couple of waste paper merchants had set up in the town by 1869 and gradually their number grew to equal the rag trade. The recycling of waste paper gained greater importance during the twentieth century, and paper mills came to rely on this commodity for their raw material. Smith, Stone & Knight decided to set up their own collection organisation. They purchased the waste paper trade carried out by J. Spicer & Sons Ltd, Great Charles Street

Above and right: Paper making at Smith, Stone & Knight. *(Local Studies Department, Birmingham Reference Library)*

in 1911, and two years later set up a new company, the Birmingham Waste Co. Ltd, to manage the collection of paper and rags. Birmingham Waste had two sites. Rags were dealt with at Clement Street, while waste paper was collected at the Moland Street depot.

Smith, Stone & Knight also began acquiring mills in other parts of the country. Avonside Mill, Bristol was purchased in 1908, while Pendleton Mill, in Manchester, was added to the group during 1917. The period 1920–39 proved to be a lean time for the company, yet resources were found to establish another bag factory in Crown Street, Bordesley, in 1927.

Bombing caused damage to Aston Mill, Union Mill and Cattells Grove Mill during the Second World War. The task of rebuilding the works commenced in 1946. The Birmingham mills remained heavily dependent on coal, and during the coal crisis of 1947 were forced to shut down until supplies returned to normal levels. Family ownership also came to an end during this period, when a public company was formed to take over the business in 1948. During 1954 a new mill was built at Cranemore Street adjacent to the Cattells Grove site where paper making was concentrated. Both Aston and Union Mills were closed down.

In 1970 Smith, Stone & Knight was bought by Dolan Packaging, which in turn was bought by the Swedish nationalised wood products company ASSI, in 1977. The Cattells Grove/Cranemore Street site was modernised and a new gas turbine combined heat and power plant was installed in 1985. ASSI sold the mill to KNP BT in 1987. Work then went ahead on the construction of a brand new mill, Paper Mill 4, which extended across the site of the old retort houses that had belonged to the closed-down Nechells Gas Works. This new mill was geared up to deal with the recycling of waste paper on a large scale. The first brown paper was produced there on 2 October 1989. The name of the company changed again in 1998 when Smith, Stone & Knight became Kappa SSK. Paper Mill 4, where the recycling of waste paper now provides the bulk of the raw material, remains part of the Saltley skyline. The Birmingham Mill remains devoted to this line of business, where rolls of recycled paper are produced for the corrugated case industry.

A VISIT TO THE KAPPA SSK, JUNE 2000

For those who travel by train between Birmingham and Derby or Leicester, the Kappa Paper Mills at Nechells form a significant landmark. The long building is easily identifiable through the columns of white steam that regularly rise skyward from the mill chimneys. The site of the mills occupies a long, rectangular strip of land that lies parallel to the railway and a new road. Part of the site comprises the old Birmingham Paper Mill works and the rest is built on a piece of ground formerly occupied by Nechells Gas Works.

Birmingham residents may be aware of the green waste-paper collection bins that are distributed throughout the city. These bins provide an important supply of material for the mills. Paper and board are also collected from a number of industrial sources, and all come together in a collection yard beside Adderley Road. Piles of waste paper also form seemingly endless columns at the Nechells Mill.

Tractors convey bucketsful of waste paper to the pulping tank, which is located at one end of the mill. Extensive screening and filtering is carried out this process, where the paper and board are mashed and broken down into fibres. These fibres are then collected for the mill. A second pulping tank adds new paper material to supplement the recycled matter. As if by some magical process, the fibres are concentrated together onto a moving mesh belt that allows liquid to drain away but retains the solid matter for the series of rollers ahead. The process is completely automated from the time the fibres enter the mill to the finished rolls cut and ready for despatch at the other end.

The mill is known as PM4, or Paper Mill 4, and dates from 1989. It occupies most of the length of the long building and is two levels high. The working machinery fills the bottom level, while the upper level houses the rollers which carry the endless sheet of paper as it is compressed and dried into new sheets 15½ft wide. At the far side of the mill the sheet is automatically cut to size and rolled up into reels. A mechanical moving platform and turntable set up each roll for distribution to the warehouse. At the time of the visit the warehouse stacking was done by forklift, but a new system of robotic delivery was in the process of being installed.

Kappa's paper mill at Saltley, March 2001. This modern plant is engaged in the recycling of paper and production of brown paper. Stacks of newspapers and other paper can be seen to the right of the main building. *(Ray Shill)*

Kappa's paper mill as seen from Saltley Viaduct, March 2001. *(Ray Shill)*

The recycling of paper and board has many environmental considerations. In recent times British society has adopted a throwaway philosophy. Increased use of packaging for food and many other goods has been accompanied by wholesale dumping of waste paper and plastics at landfill sites. Little thought was given to the cost of production or the energy used in the process. People have now regained a moral conscience and the collection of waste paper and board for recycling has been particularly encouraged during the last five years.

Kappa SSK have been very keen to tap into new ideas in this respect. It still runs a collection service and its green paper collection bins are a regular sight on street corners. Waste paper is frequently delivered to a storage yard beside Adderley Road before transfer to the main works. One radical suggestion was the use of canal boats to convey waste paper and board to Nechells. SSK had long been associated with canal transport and once owned a fleet of boats that were used to convey coal and gypsum. A load of paper was brought from London during the summer of 2000 to the Adderley Road yard. Much of the journey was made in the holds of two narrowboats.

Some paper suppliers produced specialist ranges of paper. Listed among their number were J. & W. Mitchell, whose paper factory occupied the corner of Watery Lane and Coventry Road. These works had previously been the site of the Bordesley Park Works where Dr Church was involved in the making of road locomotives for the London & Birmingham Steam Carriage Co. These premises were advertised for sale in August 1837 and were subsequently taken over by the Mitchells for the making of fancy and coloured papers.

Carr & Co. (Paper) Ltd specialised in the making of waterproof paper and packing material. The company was formed by William Carr, who first traded with his brother Arthur at Saltley as paint and waterproof paper makers. William Carr transferred the paper making business to Kealey Street.

The factory was bombed during the Second World War and work was transferred again to new premises at Shirley in 1950, where the firm concentrated on making protective packaging. The raw components were paper, glues and bitumen, waxes and other fibres. Gummed paper printed with the customer's name provided lucrative sales. The firm also sold aluminium foil.

Advertisement for J. & W. Mitchell, Bordesley Paper Works.

J. & W. Mitchell's paper factory, 1950s. *(Heartland Press Collection)*

PAPIER MÂCHÉ

The making of papier mâché (which means mashed or pulped paper) was a trade closely allied with eighteenth- and nineteenth-century Birmingham. Papier mâché trays began to be manufactured in England to copy those produced in Japan. Henry Clay deserves the credit for the establishment of British papier mâché. He discovered that layers of paper pasted together in moulds of wood or metal would compete with the Japanese article, which was then much sought after in this country. In 1772 Clay took out a patent for the making of highly varnished panels for roofs and sides of coaches and sedan chairs. Clay's material was hard and could be sawed and planed like wood. Clay worked in Birmingham as a japanner and used his invention to establish papier mâché manufacture in the town. His factory was located in Newhall Street, where he enjoyed royal patronage from the King and the Prince of Wales.

Other manufacturers entered the trade when Clay's patent expired, and papier mâché came to be made into articles of everyday use or ornament. Birmingham manufacturer Jennens & Bettridge started in the japan trade in about 1815, trading first from Lionel Street and then Constitution Hill. It made inkstands, workboxes and a number of different articles in papier mâché. For nearly forty years high quality ware was produced at its factory at 99 Constitution Hill.

Papier mâché was made from some of the best quality paper. The moulds were made from copper or tinned iron and the paper was soaked in paste made from flour and glue. The moulds were greased with Russian tallow and the paper for each layer was worked into place by hand. The mould with the first layer of paper was heated in a stove to dry it and the process was repeated with further layers of pasted paper until the required thickness was attained. The blanks were then removed from the mould and dipped in a solution that hardened them. They then spent another period in a hot stove to dry. The blanks from the stove were taken to the making-up shop to be planed and filed until their surfaces were flat and true. Layers of black varnish, or japan, were applied and with each application the blank was heated in a stove. Hand polishing completed the finish. Female workers were employed to polish the surface with pumice stones.

Papier mâché articles were noted for both art and craftsmanship. Fine and artistic designs by some of best painters were frequently incorporated into the surface of the articles. In 1825 Jennens & Betteridge took out a patent for inlaying pearl into their work. Slivers of pearl cut from shell ranging in thickness from $\frac{1}{40}$in to $\frac{1}{100}$in were fixed into the design with varnish. Other embellishment such as burnished gold could be incorporated into the designs. Further embellishment became possible with developments made in the electroplating industry, and electro-deposit work was introduced into the trade during 1844. In 1847 Benjamin Giles perfected a method for inlaying gems into the material. Papier mâché was also used as a component of imitation jet, where it was used to fashion beads and other jewellery.

Many Birmingham japaners made papier mâché wares as part of their general japan business. James McCallum and Edward Hodgson were typical of those who chose to profit from the general demand. Their factory at 147–9 Brearley Street operated during the 1840s and 1850s, but was subsequently taken over by George Ault, who made photographic cases and passe-partouts to suit the new photographic industry. The golden years of papier mâché production drew to a close during the 1850s. The firm of Jennens & Betteridge & Sons went into receivership during 1859. T.H. Jennens had left the firm to set up a rival concern in London during 1857. The elder John Betteridge had died in February 1859 and remaining members of the Jennens and Betteridge families decided after the March trading figures to petition the court of bankruptcy.

McCALLUM & HODSONS PAPIER MACHE MANUFACTORY.

Production at the Betteridge factory continued until August 1859, until many of the outstanding orders had been dealt with. Finally, in September, a sale disposed of the valuable stock of wares and blanks. The remaining finished stock included furniture. There was a 4ft diameter circular table, which was a copy of one supplied by the firm to the Emperor of Russia. Other articles in the sale included a pair of enamel gem vases which were identical to a pair manufactured for Queen Victoria; banner screens that had been exhibited at the Paris Exhibition; Indian screens; inlaid pearl and pencilled sofa tables; dress chairs; and an assortment of tea trays and waiters. The unfinished stock that included blanks in various stages of manufacture was estimated to be worth £4,000, while the patterns included hundreds of models and moulds for various designs of tea trays, workboxes, table pillars, inkstands, chair backs and desks. Once the debt had been settled, John Betteridge Jnr continued the trade, first from 96 Constitution Hill and then from 19–21 Barr Street. The works at 99 Constitution Hill were adapted for other purposes when Joseph Taylor set up the Derwent Foundry at this address. One chapter of Birmingham history may have closed there, but another was about to begin. Taylor first constructed steam engines on this site but later, in partnership with Challen, became world-renowned press makers. The nineteenth century proved to be the heyday of papier mâché production. It gradually fell out of favour, and although some manufacturers continued to specialise in the trade, production declined after 1900 and had practically ceased by 1940.

McCallum and Hodson's papier mâché factory. *(Cornish's Guide, 1853)*

BLOCK PAPER MAKERS

Birmingham had a number of manufacturers who produced block paper and pasteboard using techniques closely allied to the papier mâché trade. Paper for specialist uses was made in factories located around the town. William Brindley deserves an important share of the credit for this trade. His patents and inventions improved the manufacture of papier mâché ware and paperboard. Brindley used rags, instead of fine quality paper, as a raw material. Rags were washed and ground to make a pulp. Workmen collected the pulp in a simple mould or shallow tray, sometimes known as a deckle. The pulp in the tray was allow to drain, and then was emptied onto a felt square held in a press. The process was repeated several times until several layers of pulp had been built up to the required thickness and the press was full. The press was then put into action and water was squeezed out, leaving a uniform thick sheet of paper. Different thickness of paper was achieved by using deckles of different depths.

The paper produced might be used in making papier mâché or paperboard. A particular local use was the making of button boards. These were manufactured by passing the paper between a pair of rollers. The thick, flat sheets of board were then cut into discs of different sizes, called button blanks, which were then used as a component in the making of Florentine buttons.

For some time before the abolition of Paper Excise Duty, duty on button board was evaded by cutting the sheets into blanks before sale to the button makers. Blanks were free of government duty, but this did not stop the inspectors monitoring button board suppliers in Birmingham. Prosecutions followed when button board instead of blanks was supplied. The Birmingham button trade was then quite extensive, and several local paper makers specialised in the supply of button blanks. They invested in steam-driven presses and other machinery, using capital saved from the non-payment of excise.

An exceptionally hard form of board was achieved by dipping paperboard in linseed oil. The dipped board was heated in a japanning stove to produce a strong and firm board that was sold on to cabinet-makers and japanners to be worked up.

PAPER BUTTONS AND BEADS

Thomas William Davenport and Samuel Cole patented an improved method of making buttons, beads and picture frames in November 1861, which incorporated powdered papier mâché. Davenport and Cole were patent jet makers at the Rea Works, Balsall Heath Road and the methods developed at the Rea Works produced a variety of synthetic articles, which included artificial jet.

Jet was a form of lignite, which was found near Whitby. Once cut and polished, this black stone was prized as a semi-precious jewel. Jet jewellery found particular favour after the death of Prince Albert, when Queen Victoria wore jet as part of her mourning dress. The nation followed suit and demand for both the stone and artificial products increased.

Davenport & Cole used paper, papier mâché or dried paper pulp and ground them down to a fine powder. This powder was then mixed with a mixture or paste of some, or all, of the following materials: glue, paste, gas tar, black tar, varnish, copal varnishes, pitch, resin, gold size and oil. For some products glue and paste were sufficient to unite the paper, but the process of bead making needed strengthening, and small quantities of gas tar, varnish, paper pulp, india rubber or gutta-percha were added to the paste mix. These were particularly useful in the making of patent jet, but when a lighter colour bead was needed, copal varnish and gold size were substituted for tar. Waste papier mâché, including broken trays, was a preferred raw material, as these were already impregnated with oil and tar spirit and the resulting powder was stronger. Common sawdust was also added when greater strength was needed, especially for bulky articles. The paste was often mixed cold, but when glues were included the mixture was heated. The separate mixes were then pressed into dies and left to dry.

Davenport & Cole advertisement. *(Kelly's Directory)*

Details Patent 2935, November 1861
Davenport & Cole's Improved Composition for making buttons beads etc.

To twenty-eight pounds of varnish, which, if the composition is required black, may be tar varnish, but if coloured, must be some nearly colourless varnish, such as copal, add in a melted state five pounds and a quarter of gutta-percha, seven ounces of resin, three ounces and a half of any fat oil, and eighty-four pounds of powder black, or powder colour according to circumstances. These ingredients are to be well mixed together, when they will form a pasty compound, capable of being pressed and moulded in dies into any desired form and pattern, and when cold the articles will have sufficient strength for any of the uses above named, and may be economically employed in many branches of industrial and art manufacture.

For other uses requiring greater toughness and capacity for manipulation, such as the manufacture of twisted brooches, bracelets, chain link, and similar ornamental articles, we should prefer the composition to consist of the following ingredients: Wheaten flour, three pounds and a half; glue, one pound and a half; pulverised or ground Papier Maché, seven pounds; sheet paper reduced to pulp, two ounces; powder black or colour, half a pound. The glue is of course, to be melted, and of a consistency which may be left to judgement of the operator, and the other ingredients are to be added gradually, and the whole mass intimately combined into a state resembling dough, in which condition it may be worked into any desired form, and left to harden, or stoved if requisite.

The factory was square in shape and comprised a four-storey block on the river Rea side, but elsewhere rose to three storeys. The buildings were filled with cutting machines, drilling machines and lathes. During 1872, part of Davenport & Cole's collapsed into the nearby Rea, leading to the temporary closure of the works. Production was continued for only a few more years. By 1880 the premises had been converted into a brass foundry.

PAPER BOX MANUFACTURE

Several local firms carried on making boxes and cartons for packaging. Birmingham manufacturers were quick to adapt to the possibilities of increased sales through colourful packaging. At first boxes were put together by hand, but then mechanical means were developed to assist the manufacturer. Cadbury Brothers, chocolate makers, were the first local firm to adopt machinery for box making.

THE MANUFACTURE OF PAPER BOXES BY MACHINERY

The manufacture of paper, or pasteboard, boxes of various descriptions has of recent years developed into an industry furnishing employment to a large number of persons. There has been a great demand on the part of the retail dealers for showy goods on display on their shelves and in their shop windows, that wholesale dealers and manufacturers have been compelled to supply their merchandise in a variety of attractive packages for instance grocers, chemists, seedsmen, drapers, tobacconists, stationers, and other tradesmen vie with each other in rendering their shops as attractive as possible by this display of packages of this description, which, besides being pleasing to the eye, are found extremely convenient for immediate delivery to a customer, which the particular articles they contain are demanded. In this way the box making industry has been created, and a number of producers of staple articles, as for example, manufacturers of pens, matches, cocoa &c- make their own boxes in a branch of their establishments set aside for the purpose. Girls, chiefly, are employed in box making, and to their light and expert fingers it furnishes a suitable means of obtaining a livelihood. Quick, however, as human hands may be a machine has been invented, which will produce paper boxes with greater speed and cheapness, if not better finish, than they can be made with hand. The invention, like that of the sewing machine, is American, and has been patented by the Paper Box Machine Co. of Cleveland, Ohio. One of the company's machines has been adopted at the new works of Messrs Cadbury Brothers, at Stirchley Street, near Kings Norton, where it was seen in operation for the first time on Thursday last, by a number of gentlemen, who attended on the invitation of the vice-president and manager of the company, Mr C.E. Bolton. The machine is a remarkable piece of mechanism, consisting of a complication of parts somewhat bewildering to one unskilled in mechanical engineering, but for all of which there are uses and they work with the nicety of clockwork. The machine altogether occupies a space of about 6ft square. The principal parts of the machine are fixed to a bed plate 4ft square, with a frame moving perpendicularly. The paper or pasteboard blanks, previously cut out into the desired shapes, are passed onto the plate, as in the envelope machine. On one side is a small trough containing liquid glue, in which a roller turns, and coming into contact with two smaller rollers transfers glue to them. Having received a coating of the liquid in a manner somewhat resembling the ink roller of a printing machine, they move to the centre of the plate, where they transfer their coating to two smaller stamps, which fall on the pasteboard, and glue the edges, while simultaneously a kind of hammer falls and indents the paper where it requires folding. Two iron fingers immediately move from the opposite side of the plate, and pull the pasteboard along underneath to and instrument called a plunger, similar to a large punch, of the size and shape of the box. The plunger strikes the middle of the pasteboard through a hole in the plate, whilst a flapper and folder closes on each side of it and press all sides of the paper round the plunger. The box is then formed, except one that is left open, and in that condition it drops into a revolving wheel placed horizontally, containing twenty receivers, and is expelled by means of a rod. All this process is carried out in a much shorter space of time as it takes to describe it.

Birmingham Post, October 4th 1879

CHAPTER ELEVEN

THE TOY TRADE

Any study of Birmingham industry will reveal that before the end of the seventeenth century steel and other buttons were manufactured, and the many other articles in steel that were generally described as 'steel toys'. In fact, Birmingham was once referred to as the Toy Shop of Europe. Yet articles which included shoe buckles, snuff-boxes, bracelets and a seemingly endless variety of small ware had little connection with the modern use of the word toy, which is generally used to describe an item to be played with and from which pleasure is gained.

Until the first decades of the twentieth century children's pleasure was derived from simple needs and simple values. Toys were frequently brightly coloured robust objects made from metal or wood. It was a time before television, cinema and computer games, which have since created a much wider demand for toys and a demand often market-driven by the whim of the moment.

Birmingham had several toy makers that produced wooden, metal and soft toys. They relied on the skills of the carpenter, metal stamper, the varnish maker and paint maker to produce articles wanted by any child. William Barker & Son Ltd of 157 Irving Street specialised in brightly painted rocking horses that were once the prized possessions of

The Stanley Works were an old factory on the corner of Kent Street and Lower Essex Street built for the saddlery and saddlers' ironmongers' trade, and later adapted by Jarratt, Laughton & Rainsford for cardboard box making and the making of model building sets. *(Heartland Press Collection)*

any family and are now a distant memory. Thomas Izon had works in 57 Inge Street that made buckets and spades for those trips to the sands at the seaside. Other toy makers included Dolphin & Co., Dunn & Smith, Louis Goldberg and Montil Manufacturing Co. Ltd. Louis Goldberg of 57 Livery Street made soft toys and dolls at factories at Lionel Street and the Hurricane Works, George Street until the 1950s. They then moved to a disused clothing factory in Gas Street, which lay beside the Worcester & Birmingham Canal. The company was there for about ten years, when the toy factory was converted into a night club.

Some toy manufacturers catered for the more adventurous child. During the 1930s William Bailey (Birmingham) Ltd, Weaman Street made Kliptiko mechanical toys and Venebrik architectural toys. At the Stanley Works, Kent Street, Jarrett & Rainsford made the Studiette Range of models which was the brainchild of their manager, Howard Goldstein. These included ship model building kits for the *Golden Hind*, *Mayflower*, *Victory* and *Great Harry*. Model aeroplanes were also designed and produced in kits. The Studiette Range was manufactured up to 1940, when the space was required for wartime production lines. Chad Valley became the best-known Birmingham toy maker, catering for generations of children across the country and indeed the world. The Chad Valley business had its roots in the printing trade, but found a special niche in the toy market, in which it came to excel.

CHAD VALLEY

Anthony Bunn Johnson set up a printing and book-binding business in Lichfield Street, a narrow street that was swept away with the making of Corporation Street. Two of his sons set up a similar business in George Street. By 1897 one son, Joseph Johnson, was

The façade of the original Chad Valley Works fronted Rose Road at Harborne. (Archives Department, Birmingham Reference Library)

left to run the firm. He moved to Harborne and built a factory beside the Chad Brook. Birmingham Council approved plans for the new site in Rose Road in November 1896. The trade in stationers' goods was continued here, in addition to a new range of cardboard board games.

The Chad Valley business expanded gradually and the company went on to make a wider range of toys. The Rose Road works were modified and enlarged between the years 1920 and 1932. This involved the addition of another two floors to the original building and new building to the rear that extended as far as the railway. The company established a new factory at Shirley in 1935 and, in 1938, were appointed Toy Makers to the Queen.

Chad Valley became one the biggest makers of toys and games in the country, but remained a family business until 1950, when Chad Valley Co. Ltd was formed. The Chad Valley Works at Harborne then comprised four separate works. At the original Rose Road works, all the component parts of indoor games were made. These included many popular games such as 'Snakes and Ladders' and dominoes.

The Institute Printing Works was responsible for printing all the coloured designs for games and jigsaws, as well as labels and box tops. Chad Valley had taken over this building on a temporary basis, during the First World War, and had made the arrangement permanent in 1919. These buildings had been previously known as the

Chad Valley workers. As with many other contemporary industries, the making of toys used overhead shafting to drive the machinery. *(Local Studies Department, Birmingham Reference Library)*

Harborne and Edgbaston Institute. Its foundation stone had been laid by the actor Henry Irving. The foundation stone ceremony took place on Monday 12 August 1878 at 1.30 p.m. A special train brought people to the event from New Street station and took them back again for the luncheon held afterwards at the Masonic Hall, New Street. Construction, which amounted to £5,500 was financed by private subscription. Local builders Sapcote & Sons were awarded the contract for the Institute, and the building was completed and furnished for the inaugural soirée on 6 October 1879.

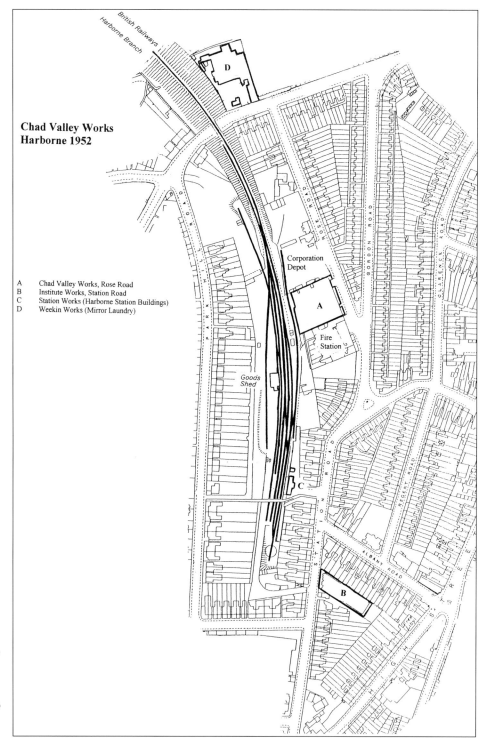

**Chad Valley Works
Harborne 1952**

A   Chad Valley Works, Rose Road
B   Institute Works, Station Road
C   Station Works (Harborne Station Buildings)
D   Weekin Works (Mirror Laundry)

Map of the Chad Valley Works, 1952. The first Chad Valley toy factory was located in Rose Road, but with increase in demand for Chad Valley products three other premises were acquired to deal with the range of toys manufactured.

Another part of the Chad Valley operation leased the old Harborne railway station. The offices and rooms within the station were used to make wooden toys and jigsaws. Harborne station was the terminus of the Harborne Railway that was constructed for a private railway company (the Harborne Railway) and opened in 1874, but operated by the London & North Western Railway and London, Midland & Scottish Railway. Passenger services ceased on a dull winter's day in November 1934. Chad Valley then leased the station and used the single passenger platform to store and season timber. The railway proved useful for the company, as it brought timber and other materials and took away parcels of finished toys.

A fourth works, near the railway over-bridge in Park Hill Road, was acquired in about 1950 from the Mirror Laundry Ltd. The laundry buildings, first erected in 1894, were renamed the Weekin Works by Chad Valley. Soft toys for babies and younger children were made here, alongside other products such as cowboy suits. Chad Valley had premises in other parts of the country. There were two factories (Wrekin & Waterloo) near Wellington, Shropshire, that made rubber toys and dolls. Another factory was located at Tat Bank, Oldbury, where teddy bears were produced.

The metal-toy manufacturing department was enlarged during 1948 when the business belonging to the aluminium holloware maker A.S. Cartwright of Western Road was acquired. This takeover was soon followed by a second, when Hall & Lane joined the Chad Valley Group. Hall & Lane produced buckets and spades, as well as many other metal products, for the Chad Valley Group.

Hall & Lane's factory, which was bounded by Dymoke Street and Leopold Street, was called the Darwin Works. It also produced a range of tin-plate articles that included oil bottles and boxes. Hall & Lane began as a partnership between Frederick Charles Hall and George James Lane. They started in business as ticket-writers and had premises in Angelina Street and later Emily Street, before the Darwin Works was founded. They produced a range of tin and enamelled tickets and window labels, which were commonly used for advertising purposes. A programme of business rationalisation was instituted by Chad Valley during the 1950s. In 1957 the Western Road Works that belonged to A.J. Cartwright was closed and their work was transferred to the Darwin Works. Chad Valley also closed the works of Gloucester toy makers Robert Brothers, which they had acquired in 1954.

Chad Valley was able to produce many different types of toys, and the design teams were constantly striving to develop new board games, jigsaws or toys. Competition in the trade was particularly acute in what was described as the 'character merchandising market' that took themes or characters from films and TV programmes. All the skills of the firm were called upon to keep up with the current trends and fads.

In 1972 Chad Valley Ltd moved to break their links with Harborne as toy making was moved to other Birmingham factories. Half of the 200-strong workforce was transferred to sister company Hall & Lane, and the rest to a new warehouse development in North Birmingham. The move was the result of reorganisation by Barclay Securities which then owned the Chad Valley Group. Barclay shut down three of the nine toy factories it owned. Wooden toy production was moved to Merton in London. Within three years the remaining Birmingham factories had also shut down, finally ending toy making by Chad Valley in the city.

CHAPTER TWELVE

BRICKMAKING & AGGREGATE TRADES

There was a time when bricks were hand made from local clays. Those engaged in the trade had a skill that was often passed down from father to son. The making of bricks was then a summer trade. Clay was dug out in the autumn and left to weather. It was 'turned' in the winter and then in the spring and summer was hand moulded, after being ground in a horse mill or trodden and kneaded by foot. The moulded bricks were then carefully stacked in a hack to dry for several days. The lengthy process of brickmaking was then completed when the dried bricks were fired in a temporary or permanent kiln heated by wood or coal. The process took several days in which to heat the bricks through and afterwards to allow the kiln to cool down so that bricks could be extracted. It was a process that made bricks of varying qualities. The yards were frequently family-run concerns and brickmakers commonly had other occupations to take them through the winter months.

The brick trade principally supplied the market for new factories and houses, but also benefited from new canal construction schemes that frequently required bricks to line the locks and tunnels and construct the aqueducts and bridges. Canal contractors working on West Midlands canals employed both stonemasons and brickmakers in the various early canal construction schemes. Bricks were fired in temporary kilns close to the construction site and were either boated or carted to the site. The trade received a further stimulus with the building of the railways. Vast quantities of bricks were needed for the building of viaducts or lining cuttings and tunnels. Permanent brickyards located in Birmingham and the Black Country now played their part in supplying this trade. Often the canal network was used to move bricks to Birmingham. Bricks, tiles and quarries were transported to central city wharves from Aldridge, Tipton, Oldbury and West Bromwich.

Mechanisation in the brick industry came in different forms. Heated drying sheds speeded up the process for drying moulded bricks. Steam-driven pug mills were devised to grind down the clay. Wire cutters were invented to slice up clay into the correct dimensions before drying and firing. But it was the complete brickmaking machines, invented during the 1850s and the 1860s, that had a major effect on the brickmaking industry. Birmingham brickmakers were slow to adopt these methods, and many remained as summer yards. These summer yards were located around the perimeter of the old town and supplied bricks, tiles and quarries to meet local needs.

Birmingham was a town and city of brick buildings and several brick yards were in existence at the same time. Working conditions were basic. The Holt Street Yard, in 1824, was located near the Old Union Mill. There was a single kiln and shed. The workers dug out the clay, hand moulded the bricks and allowed them to dry in the open air before firing. Most of the yards had a transitory existence, being developed to exploit good quality clay and closing when the clay was exhausted. Such yards were eventually covered by the housing and factory developments which they supplied.

Brick yard workers encompassed a variety of skills that ranged from the skilled moulder to the general labourer. Wages were generally low.

Brickyard Worker Wages (1872–89)
(*British Clayworker*, July 1933)

Job description	Rate of Pay
Clay getters and runners	4d to 4½d per hour
Setters and loaders	4½d to 5d per hour
Burners	5½d per hour
Moulders (for common bricks)	4s to 5s 9d per thousand
Moulders (front, or facing, bricks)	9s 6d to 11s 9d per thousand
Moulders (for 9in quarries)	20s to 23s 6d per thousand

Birmingham brick yards tended to produce red bricks, the larger quarries and some tiles. Roof tiles were a speciality of the Yardley brick yards around Hay Mills and these yards built up a reputation for their products, which were shipped by canal boat to different parts of the country. The demand for tiles was reduced during Victorian times when roofing slates from Wales became more readily available. Local yards concentrated on the production of common and facing bricks. Common bricks formed the basic structure of the buildings then under construction and vast numbers were in regular demand.

Working in a brick yard entailed a considerable amount of manual work, but some workers preferred work in the open air.

A.H. Stephenson, Recollections (*British Clayworker*, July 1933)

The conditions under which bricks were made during the first twenty years of my knowledge of the trade were extremely miserable – the only redeeming feature being that it was mainly a fresh air occupation, in contrast to some of the awful conditions in town factories. The brickyard 'hands' were a low class, ignorant, almost brutal, and with no outlook or ambition. Their earnings were small and precarious, their homes unspeakably mean and uncomfortable. They drank an altogether disproportionate amount of their wages, and took little or no thought of the morrow.

The skilled man – the Moulders – earned a greater sum of money, but spent it even more lavishly than the labourers. We had a moulder, a very skilled man, who could easily earn five pounds a week, but who drank beer literally from 'morning to night' – in fact he kept an extra boy, whose chief duty it was to keep him supplied with liquor. Very few of these men had a second suit of clothes, and would lounge about the yard, and the adjoining public houses, most of the Sunday, in the same dirty clothing in which they did their daily work. In every way it was a 'poor trade', the finished article fetching such a wretched price that it was impossible to raise the working conditions of the employees to a proper standard of living.

Brickmaking was also aided by improvements in kiln design. The early type of kiln was often known as the Scotch Kiln. These were rectangular in shape and required the fire to be lit each time bricks were admitted for baking. Continuous kilns came to be used from the late 1850s. These included the Hoffman Kiln, which was either circular or oval in shape, and were principally used to bake bricks or convert limestone to lime. The main development of the continuous kiln was the ability to heat sections of the kiln, or the whole kiln, as required. This method enabled bricks to be fired in batches and considerably increased brick production. Other variations of the continuous kiln were the Belgian, Newcastle and Staffordshire kilns. Several local brickmakers were keen to adopt the continuous kiln.

Mechanisation improved the lot of the brick yard worker and led to year-round working. The brick yards on the perimeter of the town often acquired steam engines to assist with grinding material for the moulds. Henry Harrison's yard, Highgate Street, in 1872 comprised five brickmaking sheds made from oak and deal, a 40hp beam engine and two Cornish boilers. The brick labourers worked with tools and wheelbarrows, and bricks were moulded on a group of tables.

More equipment became available in later years. The Nursery Brickworks, Holyhead Road, Handsworth, in 1883 possessed a 20hp horizontal engine, egg-ended boilers, pug mill and rolls, brick press and a semi-dry brickmaking machine in addition to the kilns and sheds.

The largest concentration of brick works was situated near Adderley Park and included the Garrison Farm Estate owned by the Digby family. The land had been arable, but uses changed with the building of a canal and the railways. Contractors working in the 1830s and 1840s for the London & Birmingham Railway, the Birmingham & Gloucester Railway, the Birmingham & Derby Junction Railway and the Birmingham & Warwick Junction Canal revealed workable clay deposits, which led to the establishment of a number of yards that extended southwards from Saltley across the estates of C.B. Adderley and Garrison Farm towards the Coventry road. This area was bisected by the London & Birmingham Railway line, with the greatest concentration of yards being located south of the line.

Brickmakers paid a royalty on the bricks made, and surviving Landor and Digby estate records have agreements for two yards, dated 1843, where a royalty of 2s per 1,000 bricks was paid to the land owner, Henry Eyres Landor. Benjamin Stych (tool maker) and Robert Masey (brickmaker) worked the smaller area. They agreed to pay the royalty on an annual make of 300,000 bricks. William Wood and Thomas Allen leased 55 acres of the Garrison Farm estate and elected to pay the 2s royalty on a make of one million bricks per year. In 1847 Henry Jackaman leased another 4 acres at Nova Close, agreeing to pay the royalty for 800,000 bricks each year.

These people must rank among the first of the brick yard owners in the district and all, it seems, would have been summer yards. Ownership changed from time to time, mainly through the rigours and hardships of keeping the yard in work. Mechanisation was introduced during the 1850s. The royalty accounts presented by Fox & Barley in 1856 reveal that brick production at their yard was conducted throughout the year.

Fox & Barley were one of three or four brick masters working the estate at this time. Other contemporary workers were brick and coal merchant, Thomas Jelliff, and William Mansfield who traded as Atlas Patent Brick & Quarry Co., Garrison Street. Mansfield took over Jelliff's yard during 1861 and operated both yards together.

Account of bricks made by Fox & Barley Brick Makers, Garrison Farm Estate _(Birmingham Library Archive Department, ref. 578875)_			
Kiln	April 1856–April 1857	May 1857–May 1858	May 1858–May 1859
1	224,000	168,000	252,000
2	40,000	147,800	80,000
3	252,000	196,000	196,000
Total	516,000	511,800	528,000

Sales plan of Albert Brickyard, 1884. Brick works had several standard features. There was the marl hole where the clay was raised, drying sheds where the formed bricks were left to dry before firing, and the kilns where the firing was done. At the Albert Brickyard, Bordesley Green, steam engines were used to raise the clay from the pit, and steam was also used for the drying sheds. Once the bricks were ready they were sent to the Hoffman continuous kiln for firing. *(Local Studies department, Birmingham Libraries)*

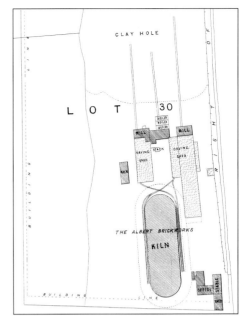

Below: Plan showing the location of the major Bordesley Green brickworks.

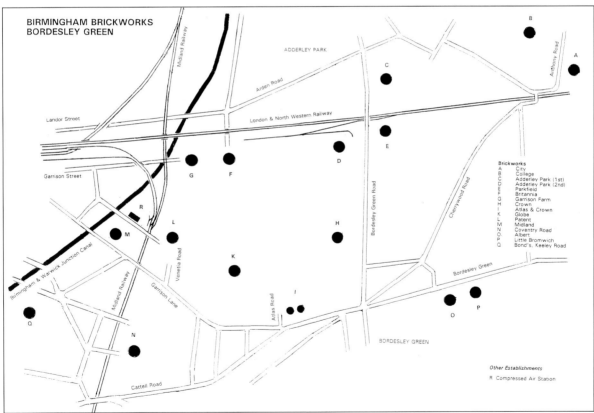

Bordesley Green was the name given to the area that bounded the Garrison Farm estate to the east and geographically located around the junction of Garrison Lane, Little Green Lane and the Bordesley Green Lane that ran northwards to Saltley. George Savage established the Albert Brickworks east of the Green in about 1878. Savage lost all his savings trying to make this business a success. The Albert Brickworks were offered for sale in February 1884. They had a Hoffman Patent Brick Kiln that could hold 500,000 bricks, three drying sheds, and three clay mills, stabling and shedding. The Bordesley

Green Brick Co. later restarted this yard and continued to make bricks there until 1902. Henry Charles Davies was manager of the yard and bricks were supplied to Davies & Simmond's builder's business. Their yard was closed when they found that bricks could be supplied more cheaply from other yards.

The Winterton family acquired an adjacent strip of land in about 1898 and built another brick yard there. They named this yard Little Bromwich and set up the Little Bromwich Brick Co. to manage the operation during 1899. The demand for bricks for new housing was constantly increasing and the new plant at Little Bromwich had a large continuous kiln, designed to produce common bricks in quantity.

The large Garrison Farm estate continued to be divided up for fresh brickmaking ventures, and established brickmakers continued to get clay from unworked land. William Mansfield decided to open a new yard near the Green, which became the Atlas Brickworks. Following Mansfield's bankruptcy in 1872, George Savage acquired the yard. Albert Humpage, a builder and developer, persuaded Savage to sell to him his interest in Atlas. The profits made by this venture encouraged other local businessmen to invest in the local brick yards. Humpage was a man who, until 1871, earned his living as an insurance agent. During that year he decided to become a speculator dealing in the purchase and sale of land. He became associated with the development of new properties in Corporation Street, which included Princes Corner, the Central Arcade, Victoria Buildings and the New Theatre. The Atlas Brickworks would have provided some of the bricks for the new ventures, but it was a limited supply for Humpage's grand designs. Humpage sold a half share to Thomas Gough and then the remainder to Jacob Sames. Humpage then invested his money in a new brickmaking venture, the Albion Vitrified Blue Brick Works, West Bromwich.

After two years' trading at the Atlas Works, Gough decided to quit the brick trade, leaving Sames with the liabilities. Sames's piano business was profitable and he was able to cover the losses at this time, but he lacked the business acumen to run the yard and few records or accounts were kept. Brickmaking was a precarious business and profit margins were slender at the best of times. Business at the Atlas Brickworks suffered, like all the other yards, through a bad trade depression and the losses were enough to force Sames into receivership during 1883.

Although speculation might have provided the finance for some ventures, the mainstay of the industry was the practical and experienced brickmakers. One who fell into this category was George Payton, who had charge of another yard, the Patent Brick & Quarry Brickworks, from about 1867 until his death in 1875. The responsibility for working the yard remained with the executors of the will until John Laughton Jnr married Payton's widow. Another yard was established between the Patent and Atlas works that became known as the Globe. John Bond started the Globe Brickworks in about 1868. He also operated yards in Dark Lane and Keeley Street.

Bond worked his yards in the summer style. During the winter months, he earned his money through other means. In his case, the winters were spent preparing malt and brewing beer. W.R. Wills, Edward Townley, R.C. Wright and Walter Dauncey formed a syndicate to buy Bond's brickmaking plant in Garrison Lane, and the Globe Brick & Tile Co. Limited was formed in 1875. They made moulded bricks, best facings, and a special machine was devoted to the grinding and preparation of special clays for this purpose. During 1896 a brickmaking machine, a continuous kiln and steam drying sheds were added to the plant. The Globe Brickworks was closed from 1915 to 1919 for the war effort, but restarted after the war and remained in use till about 1931.

A fourth yard in Garrison Lane was the Midland Works, which lay between the Midland Railway and Warwick & Birmingham Canal. Wharf facilities were provided for canal transport of the bricks made here. There was a limited supply of clay and once this was worked out production was moved to Garrison Farm Brickworks. John, and later James, Denston worked a fifth yard that extended south from Garrison Lane alongside the east side of the railway to the Coventry road. The Denstons had the yard during the 1860s, but during 1869 Josiah Derrington took over production. Contemporary maps show sheds and a bank of three kilns facing St Andrew's Street and another, smaller yard with two kilns near the Coventry road. Derrington's mill was worked by steam power and this yard continued to make bricks through to about 1892. The land was later sold to the Birmingham City Football Club, who built a new football ground there.

There were another two yards on the Garrison Farm estate, which lay close to the London & Birmingham Railway line. A corner of the available brick yard area was lost during the early 1860s when the Midland Railway had a link line built to join their Bristol and Derby railways. The railway construction changed the local geography. Garrison Street was extended across the new railway on the level to form a new access to Mansfield's brickyard. William Riddell & Co. purchased Garrison Farm Brickworks during 1869, when Mansfield transferred his business to the new Atlas site. Garrison Farm Brickworks had canal access and railway sidings and both Riddell and his successor, W.H. Hancox, did a large trade, with canal bricks being run by barrow straight from the kilns into boats. Poor trading eventually forced Hancox into bankruptcy and agents working for the land owners managed this yard until the Midland Brick Co. took charge of the works.

During 1905 Frederick Welch Barrows, on behalf of the Midland Brick Co. Ltd, signed a new agreement for the yard with Charles Digby agreeing to pay a rent of £600 per year and a royalty of 1s 6d per 1,000 bricks produced. The plant then included a 45hp steam engine that drove a clay-grinding machine. Production was increased when a modern Belgian kiln replaced the old kilns. The Midland Brick Co. also absorbed the Britannia Works adjoining the yard, run by John James, and installed a machine and continuous kiln there. The Britannia yard derived its name from Brown & Marshall's Railway & Carriage Works that were located opposite. Access to this yard was from Landor Street. James had the yard for a number of years. His main business was farming, and the management of the yard was left to his clerk.

Another four brick yards faced the Bordesley Green Road near Adderley Park. The earliest yard was set up for John Burk on a strip of land north of the railway. John Burk, his widow and later Elson, Burk & Co. worked this yard throughout the 1860s and early 1870s. The Adderley Park Brick Co. Ltd, formed in 1876, then took over operation of the yard. Plant was brought up to date by erecting a steam-driven grinding mill. This company established a new brick yard across the road and erected new plant there. The new works were served by rail and specialised in making front and moulded bricks. The original yard was closed and the disused marl pit was used by the Wolseley Car Co. to test their vehicles. The land was subsequently levelled and used by Wolseley to build the East Works. Adderley Park Brick Works continued to make bricks through the 1930s. Thomas Ward, scrap merchants, subsequently took over the premises.

The Parkfield Brickworks were opened for C.P. Bond during the early 1880s and were operated under the name of the Parkfield Brick Co. until 1908. Theirs was a small yard that lay close to Adderley Park railway station. The marl pit was filled in and the site incorporated into extensions made to the Calthorpe Motor Car Factory and Mulliner's Car Body Workshops.

Crown Brickworks were located south of the Adderley Park New Brickyard and were worked by Henry Chare. He had made his money making window blinds and had decided to pursue a new venture. Like so many other contemporary brick yard owners, Chare found it a daunting challenge. He returned to the furniture trade and allowed the Atlas & Crown Brickworks Co. to take over the plant. This new company was formed by the acquisition of the Crown and Atlas works during 1883. New mechanised plant was installed and each yard had a circular continuous kiln. Atlas Works closed before 1900 and Crown ceased production before 1905.

Nock's Brickworks, Holly Lane, Erdington. The drying sheds and incline house are visible in this view. *(Heartland Press Collection)*

Below: Aerial view of Castle Bromwich Brickworks. A feature of the Birmingham brick trade was the adoption of specialist kilns such as the Hoffman type for bulk production. *(Archives Department, Birmingham Reference Library)*

The clayfield extended northwards to Saltley and there were two yards near Saltley College. The College Brickworks was located near Bridge Road and faced St Peter's College, from which it gained its name. This yard was owned by another member of the Payton family, Peter. The plant, described in 1878, included three kilns and two drying sheds. The other yard was the City Brickworks and Tileries in Anthony Road. It was started by John Garlick, railway contractor, but stood idle after Garlick's failure in 1884. Mr Bond reopened it in the 1890s, when a wire-cutting machine was installed. John Lewis and later the City Brick Co. Ltd had this yard. A continuous kiln was installed there after 1900.

An early yard was the Heath Brickworks, owned by Richard Taylor. This yard was near the Midland Railway and Birmingham & Warwick Junction Canal, but had closed before 1880. Production was moved to a new yard situated beside Common Lane and Washwood Heath Lane, which was operated by Taylor & Hales and later Edward Hales.

Further east, a small yard and a single kiln were worked beside Black Pit Lane, Bromford. In 1912 Mr Winteron leased land beside Bromford Lane from Viscount Newport to put down a large brickmaking plant, which included drying sheds and a continuous kiln. These works were operated by the Castle Bromwich Brick Co. Ltd and remained in use until about 1967. Erdington had several small yards, which dated back to the early years of the nineteenth century, but one, at Holly Lane, was developed for large-scale production of bricks. William Nock owned this yard and it was continued in his name until about 1952.

There were a number of brick works located on the southern side of the city. There were a group of yards around Greet and Tyseley. Arthur Lewis started a yard at Greet that bordered on Percy Road and Warwick Road. The name of this yard was Burbury, evidently derived from a former yard Lewis had in Burbury Street. When Lewis first had this yard, surface clay was hand puddled and then ground in a horse mill; bricks were moulded by hand and dried in the sun. Lewis erected a 'Staffordshire Mill' and a range of drying sheds, but bricks continued to be moulded by hand until a wire cutting machine was installed. Lewis made large quantities of bricks in the hope of selling them all. He also kept a large stable of horses for the delivery of his bricks.

In 1917 A.H. Stephenson purchased the Greet Brickworks and he went into partnership, in 1919, with C.H. Barrows and Ernest Swain to form a private company, the Burbury Brick Co. Ltd, and finance was obtained to erect a continuous kiln. The clay was ground and delivered to a brickmaking machine by a travelling belt. From there the formed bricks were sent to the drying sheds. After forty-eight hours the dried bricks were conveyed to one of the sixteen chambers within the kiln for burning. The machinery was driven by electricity and the clay hole lit by electricity. Shelters were provided for the clay getters to ensure production in winter and summer alike. Greet Brickworks were closed and demolished during 1962.

Henry Hemming established the Waterloo Brickworks, Speedwell Road in 1895. There was a drying shed heated by exhaust and live steam and a continuous Belgian kiln. Hemmings eventually sold out to Frank & William Bayliss, who continued the making of bricks there until 1969, operating finally as the Birmingham Brick Co. Ltd. Clay was dug out of the pit with hand picks and shovels, then moved by light railway to the base of the incline that carried the clay up to the mill. Bayliss was one of a number of Birmingham brickworks that chose to automate the clay getting process. Castle Bromwich, Greet, Kings Heath, Kings Norton and Nock's all adopted mechanical diggers and light railway locomotives on the tramways to bring the clay to the mills. Bayliss was the last to use a locomotive delivery system. By 1968 the marl pit had reached a depth of 125ft, but was waterlogged. One locomotive was retained to haul clay-laden skips along a level section of track that ran alongside the edge of the quarry straight to the mill.

Derrington & Sons was an old established firm, which began when Edward Hales and Josiah Derrington formed a brickmaking partnership at Primrose Hill, Duddeston. Hales was a practical brickmaker and moulded bricks by hand using clay ground by a horse working a circular track. This yard closed in about 1864, and in that year Derrington & Hales took a lease of land in Leopold Street from the trustees of the Vaughton estate. Various yards were established there to enable the building of several streets and factories.

Josiah Derrington later set up an independent venture, first at the Midland Brick Works, Garrison Lane, then at Hay Mills. Two yards were acquired at Hay Mills. The first had belonged to Reuben Shipway, who was a Berkshire builder. Shipway came to

Hay Mills to start a brickworks in Speedwell Road during the 1850s. The Shipway family then ran the yard until 1889, when it was sold to Derrington, who suffered severe losses here after the pit was flooded out during 1899. Derrington also acquired the adjacent No. 2 works from Powley & Co. in about 1890. Bricks were hand moulded at these yards until about 1896, when a wire cutting machine was installed. Brickmaking was only part of Derrington's business. He also built up a successful builders' merchants business at Dartmouth Street. Both Hay Mills yards were disposed of during the 1920s to Birmingham Corporation, who used the land for rubbish tips.

Kings Heath had two brick yards at Millpool Hill, one of which was located beside the Stratford-upon-Avon Canal near the Alcester Road bridge. Another brickmaking area was located on the west side of Kings Heath, in Kings Road. The Kings Road site was an extensive one and three separate works existed there. The original yard was established about 1878, when the plant was capable of making 65,000 bricks per week. There was a steam-driven grinding mill, a pressed brick machine and three kilns. Hough & Co. Ltd ran Kings Heath Brickworks until closure in 1960.

Hough's operation at Kings Heath was established by John Hough, who was also associated with the running of the Kings Norton Brick Works in Wharf Road, Kings Norton. These works lay close to the Worcester & Birmingham Canal, which provided a means of transport for their bricks. There was a continuous kiln here and bricks continued to be made until 1959. Clays were first worked in this district to supply the temporary kilns used to build the canal between 1795 and 1797. A large quantity of bricks was required to make West (Wast) Hill Tunnel.

Northfield had several small brick pits near the Bristol road that operated during the nineteenth century. One large yard with drying sheds and a kiln was owned by the railway and building contractors Gowing & Ingram, who used its products in their construction contracts.

Other brickmaking plants were located near California, where the Dudley Canal entered the hillside at Lapal Tunnel. Four brick yards were established in this area, three being at California and a fourth on the canal side near Weoley Castle. The first to be established was the Weoley Castle Yard, which began as a quarry wharf. A tramway was in place by 1840 for bringing stone from the quarry to the Dudley Canal. This tramway also served a clay hole and it was clay made into bricks that subsequently became the main traffic from the Weoley Castle wharf. The next works to be established was the Stonehouse Brickyard that was erected on the canal side near to the tunnel portal. Here, drying sheds and kilns were erected, and a tramway brought clay from a marl pit at California, on the other side of Stonehouse Lane. This tramway passed under the lane in a brick-lined tunnel. Isaac Flavel owned the Stonehouse yard during the 1850s and set up a canal trade in bricks to a depot in Gas Street, Birmingham. James Smart succeeded Flavel during the 1860s and it was in Smart's name that the brick yard was better known. Another title was that of the California and Lapal Brickworks. Smart died in 1892 and at that time the works comprised thirteen kilns, together with ovens, drying and stacking sheds. Following the death of Smart, these works were continued as James Smart & Sons and later James Smart & Sons Ltd. A continuous Belgian kiln replaced the earlier kilns and production was continued here through to the 1950s.

The Birmingham Patent Brickworks took clay from a marl hole adjacent to Smart's and conveyed the clay to the works that were located alongside Stonehouse Lane. Here seven kilns were erected to burn the bricks. These works changed hands after 1877 and were subsequently owned by William Ward. The third works were set up by the Lapal Brick & Tile Co. Ltd, and the builder and contractor John Garlick was secretary of the company. The Lapal works had a relatively brief independent existence. Bricks from these works were conveyed by a tramway through a tunnel and onto a wharf beside the canal. William Raybould operated another brick yard in this area. This yard faced

Adamant plaster works, Commercial Street. A carefully posed shot shows deliveries of plaster ready to leave the works. The rear of the premises bordered on Granville Street wharf, used by Doulton & Co. for the storage of pottery and glazed stoneware. *(Birmingham Art & Industry Journal)*

Harborne Park Road and took clay from land that bordered on Harborne Reservoir and Harborne Mill.

Regulations and legislation regarding thermal insulation, which led to the replacement of common bricks with concrete blocks during the 1960s, had a marked effect on the brickmaking trade. The remaining Birmingham brickmakers, whose staple trade was the making of common bricks, decided to close their yards.

OTHER BUILDING MATERIALS

The aggregate trade is a complex area that deserves further study. An essential requirement for building was cement made from limestone. Birmingham did not have limestone quarries, but limestone was available locally at Dudley, Long Itchington, Southam, Walsall and Wilmcote. It was brought by canal boat to canal-side lime kilns based on the outskirts of the town. Later commercial cements, plasters and mortars were produced that were brought into Birmingham by road, rail or canal.

The Adamant Plaster Co. Ltd, at Commercial Street, made a durable plaster. They took over the disused Washington Foundry, formerly used for casting brass and iron goods, and converted the premises for plaster making. Production commenced in about 1890. The plaster trade remained at this location for some forty years and operated under different titles that included the Adamant & Asphalt Ltd, Midland Adamant Co. and Asphalt Cement Co. The name 'Adamant' was derived from the word meaning 'exceptionally hard'.

The firms of Val de Travers–Birmingham and Midland Val de Travers Paving Co. were established in August 1871 to capitalise on the trade in bituminous rock from the mines of Val de Travers at Neuchatel, Switzerland. The material had been exclusively used in Paris since 1854 and many of the principal streets of the French capital were paved with it. A London-based Val de Travers Ltd first obtained the United Kingdom rights, and it was they who arranged for the Midland company to market the paving locally. Their works were located at Aston beside the canal and Plume Street. Street paving provided the core of their business, but surfacing skating rinks also provided additional revenue.

CHAPTER THIRTEEN

THE AIRCRAFT INDUSTRY

BALLOONS AND AIRSHIPS

Balloons were developed for commercial and military purposes. The firm of Richard H. Taunton & Hayward of Star Tube Works, Heneage Street, made engineering parts for war balloons, whose uses included the assessment of troop positions and movements. Howard Lane & Co., engineers, of 28 Heneage Street, developed a new type of balloon for the Italian government and, specifically, the Massowah Expedition. The balloon was built in Birmingham using ox-skin for the gas bag, and employed a patent method developed by Lane for sealing the skins together. Over 15,000 skins were required to make the 6,500cu ft capacity bag. This balloon was assembled at a secret location, which was later revealed to be Belmont Hall, and in addition to the gas bag involved the making of the net and car. When completed, the balloon was filled with hydrogen gas and tested at Aston Lower Grounds, in November 1887.

The British government became interested in the tests and detectives were employed to investigate the company affairs. The British Army had military balloons and the new Lane Balloon was considered to have included equipment based on, or practically identical with, the balloon equipment of the British Army. Major J. Templer, second-in-command at the Aeronautical School at Chatham, was charged with divulging information that should have been kept secret. The major faced court martial proceedings, but was exonerated when alleged visits to Belmont Hall could not be proved. The crucial part of the prosecution case involved the cylinders, or tubing, for the storage of hydrogen. The tubes used by Lane were shown to be the fruits of a design by M. Delmard, Nordenfelt Gun & Ammunition Co. Ltd, and made by Taunton & Hayward. It was generally accepted that British Army and Delmard had been working independently to the same end result.

Richard Hobbs Taunton was born at Wareham, Dorset, the son of Edmund Taunton. He had moved to Birmingham with his parents in 1838. Richard later became a pupil of King Edward's School and seemed destined for a career in the Church until his father's objections finally convinced him to follow another career. He entered the services of Fox, Henderson & Co., structural engineers, of the London Works, Smethwick and became one of the firm's superintendents of outdoor work. He was given the task of overseeing the erection of the roofing at Sheerness Dockyard. Taunton later assisted the head engineer with the erection of the roof for the London & North Western station at Birmingham New Street. When Fox, Henderson got into financial difficulties, Taunton was forced to seek employment elsewhere. He was appointed manager of the foundry department of Cochrane & Co., Woodside Ironworks, Brierley Hill, and for them superintended the erection of various bridges. In 1862 Richard Taunton bought the Star Tube Works, Heaneage Street, and commenced to make tubes for various purposes, and in particular seamless tubes for stationary and locomotive boilers. One of the products was the high-pressure tube made for the Government Balloon Department.

The demand for cold-drawn tubes and an increasing need for tubes to supply the bicycle industry encouraged Taunton to form a limited company. Lane and Delmard became directors in the firm of Taunton, Delmard & Lane. Disputes between the directors led to a fall in sales and receivers were appointed during 1891. A new firm, the Star Tube Co. Ltd, was formed to take over the Heneage Street works and Taunton evidently then ceased to be associated with the enterprise.

Dirigible balloons, or airships, were a product of the twentieth century. The gas bags were held in a rigid metal frame while motors and cabin were slung below. Birmingham manufacturer Joseph Lucas supplied starter motors for the six engines fitted to the R31, the first rigid airship made in Britain. They also supplied starter motors for the R34.

AEROPLANE MANUFACTURE

Birmingham ingenuity was at the heart of the revolution that brought aircraft to the skies. It was a participation that relied on the skills of the city. Early aircraft were very basic, comprising wood, steel tube, steel rope and fabric. Engineering and the ability to fashion metals placed the manufacturers in Birmingham in a position to supply components for both aircraft and airships.

A key element was the aeroplane motor, and a pioneer in this trade was the Wolseley Tool & Motor Co. of Adderley Park, whose principal trade was the production of motor cars and commercial vehicles. Their parent company was Vickers, which was later to become a well-known name in the aircraft industry. Wolseley helped to set Vickers on this path through their engine-making department at the Adderley Park Works. By 1909 work on the new engine had reached such a stage that it was ready for commercial production.

Birmingham and the New Industry (*Birmingham Weekly Post*, 2 October 1909)

At the works of the Wolseley Motor Co. a good deal of attention is being devoted to the manufacture of engines for aeroplanes and airships. These engines are now made for English and Foreign makers of aeroplanes; and at the present time one engine is being fitted to a new French 'plane', and two engines to planes of English manufacture. 'You may take it from me', said the manager of the firm, 'Birmingham is not behind in the matter. The experimental stage, so far as my firm is concerned, is over. We are satisfied as to the possibilities of the new industry.' The company mentioned was manufacturing aeroplane frames at Crayford.

Another local motor manufacturer to develop an interest in an aeroplane engine was the firm of Maxfield & Co., Victoria Road, Aston. Alfred P. Maxfield took the development one stage further through building models and a working aircraft, which he tried out at the golf links at Castle Bromwich in October 1909. Butterfield Brothers, who made engines and motorcycles at the Levis Works, Stechford, also made an engine for an experimental aircraft in 1911.

Birmingham firms did not become associated with the general assembly of complete aircraft until the onset of the First World War, when necessity dictated it. Wolseley continued to manufacture aero-engines, but also assembled complete craft for the

An Austin Whippet aircraft K158, together with the designer, J. Kenworthy. *(Austin Advocate)*

A Handley Page 0/400 J2551, built at the Birmingham Railway & Carriage Factory, Handsworth, stands alongside the Austin Whippet aircraft. *(Mike Oliver)*

fledgling Royal Flying Corps. The Austin Motor Co. at Longbridge, the Birmingham Railway & Carriage Co., Middlemore Road, Smethwick and Daimler, Carlyle Road all became associated with aircraft manufacture.

Austin made aero-engines and aircraft during First World War. The engine was of the Austin-Curtis design. Complete aircraft were RE7, RE8 and SE5a for Royal Flying Corps. Austin had a lot of adjacent land at its disposal and levelled an area for a flying field and erected flying sheds for the storage of the new craft. Birmingham Railway & Carriage Co. put to use land in Middlemore Road in 1917 to accommodate Handley Page and de Haviland aircraft; the company had contracted to build Handley Page 0/400 bombers, bi-planes and the de Haviland DH100. The BRC ceased aircraft production after the war, but Austin continued to make light aircraft that included the Kestrel, Olympic and Whippet.

The extensive and ongoing re-armament in Germany encouraged the government of the day to start a programme of new aircraft factory building. Known as the Shadow Factory scheme, the concept was originated by the Air Ministry some years before the Second World War and first took shape in the Midlands. Light alloys and components played their part. Midland mill products included extrusion, stamping, forging, sheet and strip metals and light alloys.

Austin began negotiations to acquire 23 acres of land from local farmers in Groveley Lane, Cofton Hackett for an engine factory. Work began in August 1936 for buildings

HRH the Prince of Wales's visit to the new Cofton Hackett factory. *(Austin Advocate)*

An aerial view of the extensive Nuffield aircraft factory, as seen from the Kingsbury Road, looking towards the LMS railway. *(Birmingham Museum & Art Galleries)*

Plating parts at the Nuffield factory, Castle Bromwich. *(Birmingham Museum & Art Galleries)*

that measured 1,530ft by 410ft and covered 20 acres. Austin at Longbridge extended the works by adding additional buildings and plant. The airframe factory erected later covered another 15 acres, with an adjoining flight shed of 500ft by 190ft, where completed aircraft were housed prior to testing. Construction of the Cofton Hackett Airframe Factory was completed by 1938. Engine production had commenced in time for the visit of King George VI to the factory. The first plane was completed and delivered to the Air Ministry during July 1938. Work went ahead with another two shadow factories in the Birmingham area, which were built for Rover at Acocks Green (begun in 1936) and Solihull (1938). Other factories were completed at Stokes Green (Rootes Securities–Humber), Radford (Daimler) and Canley (Standard Motor Co.).

A totally independent venture was constructed at Castle Bromwich for Lord Nuffield. During May 1938 Lord Nuffield had an interview with the Air Minster, Sir Kingsley Wood, in which he offered the services of himself and his company, Morris Motors, for the accelerated production of aircraft. The offer was accepted and Lord Nuffield quickly made arrangements for the construction of a new aeroplane factory. A 130-acre site was selected next to the Castle Bromwich Aerodrome. The Dunlop Rubber Co. had sold the land to Birmingham Corporation in 1936 and 1,100 new homes were intended to be built on the land.

Birmingham City Council had a difficult decision to make, whether to allocate land purchased from Dunlop Rubber Co. for housing or to sell it for development of a new aircraft factory that promised up to 15,000 new jobs. The Council meeting held on 31 May 1938 elected to sell the land to Nuffield. The work of land clearance and building began almost immediately after permission had been given. Sir Kingsley Wood arrived at Castle Bromwich Aerodrome by aeroplane for the ceremony to cut the first sod for the new factory on 12 July 1938.

Spitfire assembly at the Castle Bromwich plant. Fuselages for new Spitfire planes are arranged geometrically across the floor of the assembly shop. *(Birmingham Museum & Art Galleries)*

The buildings were quickly erected, and finished the next year. Vickers Ltd was given the task of managing the plant. The Castle Bromwich factory became involved in the construction of Spitfire aircraft and Lancaster bombers, which were assembled in the long building there. Complete aircraft were taken across the road to the Castle Bromwich Aerodrome for testing and trial. No words can properly describe the debt of gratitude owed by the British people to Lord Nuffield and Sir Kingsley Wood, who acted quickly to get this aircraft assembly built before the war, or the services provided by the factory in making the Spitfire aircraft, which were so crucial to the defence of Britain during the war.

Part of the credit must also be shared with the many other local manufacturers. Shadow production of aero-engines by Bristol Mercury engines was distributed among five firms, Rootes, Austin, Daimler, Standard and Rover. Austin supplied crankshafts, reduction gears and control gears. The Austin Airframe factory produced Fairey Battle aircraft for the Air Ministry, and over 1,000 were produced at Longbridge between 1938 and December 1940. Some 700 Four-Engine Stirling bombers were made. From May 1943 the company switched to Avro Lancaster and some Hurricane Mark II. Horsa gliders were also produced. The large bombers were transported in sections to a new factory at Bickenhill Lane, Marston Green, where they were assembled. Completed craft were taken from the factory across a bridge that spanned the LMS railway, to the adjacent runways at Sheldon Airport.

From 1943 BRC made giant Hamilcar gliders, which had a wingspan of 110ft and a fuselage length 68ft 6in, at their Smethwick factory. During 1945 this firm also produced two Albemarles, made with a magnesium body shell.

Midland aircraft production, and especially the components, engines and complete aircraft supplied to the Royal Air Force, was integral to the war effort. Factories in

Both the Spitfire fighter plane and the Lancaster bomber made a vital contribution to the British war effort. Lancaster bombers are seen being assembled in this photograph. *(Birmingham Museum & Art Galleries)*

Birmingham, Coventry and the Black Country constructed parts for Spitfire and Lancaster aircraft. Over 11,000 Spitfires were produced in the Midlands. There was also a substantial production of Lancaster bombs, bomb gear, machine guns and ammunition. Midland workers also made the bulk of the requirement for aircraft steel tubes, and almost half of the supply of fabricated light alloy and steel drop-forging.

Spitfires at Castle Bromwich. *(Birmingham Museum & Art Galleries)*

Birmingham metal workers helped found the aircraft making industry. James Booth & Co. was founded about 1866. They built up a reputation for making brazed tubes for the furnishing trade. Their business developed to make solid drawn tubes and rolled metal. During 1914, Booth started to draw and extrude a new aluminium alloy which was known as Duralumin. This alloy was to become an important constituent for all-metal aircraft. Electric Ordnance & Accessory Co., another Vickers-owned company, also produced Duralumin products at their Cheston Road works.

James Booth & Co. (1915) Ltd was formed to provide additional capital for development, and during the First World War considerable extensions were made to their works in Sheepcote Street and Argyle Street. From 1939 parts for aircraft were made at a new factory at Tile Cross. The factory cost £1 million and occupied a 30-acre plot. There were two main sections to the works: one part was devoted to Booth's standard production range, while the other was an Air Ministry factory for light metal alloys. The land was purchased in October 1938 from Birmingham Corporation.

The James Booth Kitts Green Factory returned to peacetime use after 1945. Alcan Plate at Kitts Green was the result of the merger of Alcan Industries with James Booth, and became the sole supplier of aluminium alloy plate in the UK. They pioneered the development of high technology material particularly for airframe construction and armour plating. This company came to have the largest plate rolling mill in Europe. Some £500,000 was invested in the project during 1960. Loewy Engineering Co. from Bolton supplied the 148in, 4-high mill.

Booth also produced specialised foil for containers and industrial use. The BAC 1–11, European Airbus and all military aircraft have used machined Alcan Plate for their main structures. Concorde and the European Space Lab Project required the development of a special structural plate that was resistant to high temperatures. Alcan Plate was also a world leader in the supply of aluminium armour plate, which was used in missiles such as the Alvis Scorpion.

Another postwar development in Birmingham was a branch of Lucas Industries, which became known as Lucas Aerospace. They made a complete range of aircraft generating systems and switch gear, engine starting, de-icing, flying controls, engine management, thrust reversers and combustion systems, instrument lighting, cockpit transparencies, and land and marine defence systems.

Lucas had three aircraft factories in the Birmingham area. These were at Shaftmoor Lane, York Road and Marston Green. With the break-up of the Lucas empire, these works passed to TRW, but are now run by A.E. Goodrich. York Road remains the major aviation plant making parts for engine management systems. The Marston Green Works now generally deal with repairs and maintenance.

CHAPTER FOURTEEN

EXHIBITIONS
FOR THE WORLD

An essential part of promoting Birmingham industry was the trade exhibitions that regularly took place. There were a number of venues distributed around Birmingham where trade exhibitions were held. They included the Birmingham Town Hall, built in 1834, Bingley Hall (1850) and Curzon Hall (1865).

Exhibitions were, at first, restricted affairs. When the British Association for the Advancement of Science held a meeting in Birmingham during August 1839 many of the events were restricted to members of the Association, who paid for tickets to attend specific events. Different branches of science and industry were assigned different sections and the exhibits were held at a number of venues. These included the Atheneum Rooms, the library of King Edward's School and the Copper Co. Rooms in Canon Street. General meetings that the public could attend were held in the Town Hall. Visits and excursions were included during the week that the events took place. Members of the Association had the opportunity to travel by packet boat along the line of the Birmingham Canal to visit the limestone caverns at Dudley or the nearby works of the Horseley Iron Co. and Barrows & Hall. This first British Association Exhibition held in Birmingham had few exhibits, and relied on models to illustrate many designs.

Ten years later a more lavish exhibition, or exposition, was organised by the British Association in Birmingham, that was to set the standard for all that followed. This exhibition was held during September 1849 and took place in the grounds of Bingley House, Broad Street, which had formerly been the residence of the Lloyd Family.

Plans were already being made for a National Exposition in London, and local businessmen intended the Birmingham Exposition to be a model for the national event that would take place in 1851. The Bingley House Exposition comprised temporary wooden buildings as well as the rooms of the house itself.

The main hall was described as follows:

The effect of the first view of the Exposition Room is remarkably striking. The visitor is suddenly introduced into a magnificent hall, 124 feet long by 90 ft broad, into which pours a flood of light from the windows at the sides and the ends, and also from an ample range of clerestory windows. Before him are spread in rich profusion, yet in perfect order, the manufacturers of Birmingham and many other towns in various parts of the Kingdom. Bronzes, lamps, chandeliers, magnificent wood carvings, gold, silver, bronze, and iron castings, meet the eye at every turn; while rich-coloured and crystal glass dazzles him with its sparkling brilliancy. In the centre of the apartment a magnificent glass candelabrum rises to the height of twenty-one feet, and further on, glancing over a rich display of papier mâché ware, and carved furniture, the eye is carried to a splendid arrangement of ecclesiastical ornaments and church furniture, over which rise, in chastened beauty, three stained windows, set as it were in a net-work of rich paper-hangings and embossed stuffs, sparkling with colours and splendid in their effect. Nor, wandering over the intervening space and turning to the entrance, does the scene there presented discredit the other portions of the Exposition. Magnificent tapestries and carpets and gorgeous hanging, serve as a frame-work for three other stained windows, and as a background for a noble display of gas-fittings, and ornamental brass-work for upholstery. Nor is this all, for a long corridor, reaching to Bingley House, and several rooms in that edifice itself, are also occupied for Exposition purposes.

(*Birmingham Gazette*, 3 September 1849)

The Exposition of 1849 proved to be a success and led to arrangements being made for a permanent exhibition hall on the site. The materials of the house, boundary walls and the temporary exhibition hall were offered for sale on 22 February 1850 and the site was subsequently cleared. Bingley House and grounds occupied an area of about 1.5 acres and was bounded on all sides by public roads. The new hall was named Bingley Hall, after the house that had formerly stood on the site.

BRITISH ASSOCIATION FOR THE ADVANCEMENT OF SCIENCE,
BIRMINGHAM
THE EXHIBITION of WORKS of MANUFACTURES and ART, connection with the ensuing GENERAL MEETING of this ASSOCIATION, will be opened at

BINGLEY HOUSE
BROAD-STREET, BIRMINGHAM
On MONDAY NEXT, the 3rd of SEPTEMBER

————

THE EXHIBITION will consist of SPECIMENS of ARTICLES of UTILITY and ORNAMENT in METALS, GLASS, CHINA, EARTHENWARE, WOOD, and WOVEN FABRICS; MODELS of MACHINERY and SCIENTIFIC APPARATUS; AGRICULTRAL IMPLEMENTS; and some INTERESTING PROCESSES of MANUFACTURE in OPERATION

————

Members and Associates of the Association will have free admission.
The public will be admitted on payment of One Shilling each person. Season Tickets, Five Shillings Each.
Open from Ten a.m. until Ten p.m.
All CONTRIBUTIONS intended for the Exhibition must be forwarded immediately, addressed to the Exhibition Committee, Bingley House, Birmingham.
The Carriage upon all Articles, which are accepted will be paid both ways by the Committee, who will also insure the articles against fire; the Committee cannot, however, hold themselves a responsibility for any damages, which may occur to the Contributions in Transit or in the Exhibition, but the utmost care will be taken of them.

WESTLEY RICHARDS, Chairman
W.P. MARSHALL & GEORGE SHAW, Honorary Secretaries

Birmingham, August 27, 1849

(Birmingham Gazette, 27 August 1849)

Money for the exhibition hall was raised by share subscription, each share having the value of £100. The local building contractors, Branson & Gwyther, of Belmont Row, erected the building at a cost of £6,000. The Hall was nearly square, being 224ft by 212ft, and had ten entrance doors, five in King Edward's Place and five in King Alfred's Place. The hall was constructed so that it could be divided into five separate compartments and had a capacity for between 20,000 and 25,000 people. A useful feature of the building was the ability to alter the internal compartments to the requirements of the show. Three streets bounded the hall buildings: King Edward's Place, Cambridge Street and King Alfred's Place. A square of land that faced Broad Street was given over for other purposes, part of which was occupied by the Prince of Wales Theatre.

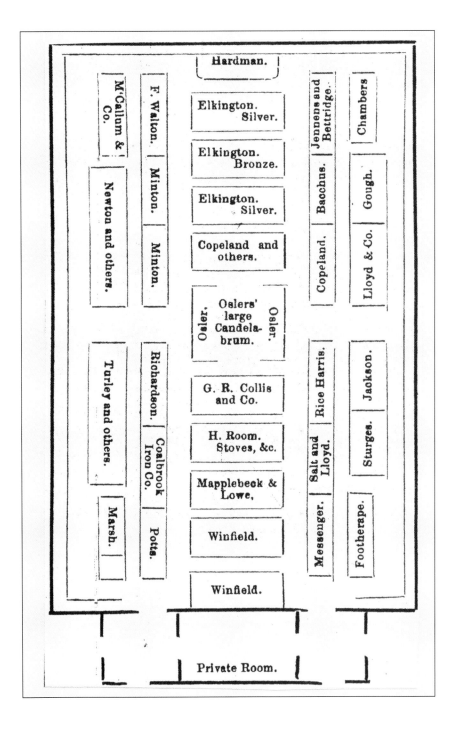

The second British Association visit to Birmingham in 1849 resulted in an exhibition which paved the way for the Great Exhibition at the Crystal Palace, London, in 1851. A temporary hall was made in the grounds of Bingley House where the exhibitors' stands were arranged to the plan published. *(Birmingham Journal, 1 September 1849)*

Bingley Hall was principally used for exhibitions and cattle, pigs and poultry shows. Livestock shows were a recent development for Birmingham, and had previously been held in temporary accommodation. The first show for poultry, fat pigs and store pigs was held at Thomas Bretherton's Horse & Carriage Repository in Worcester Street, in December 1848. Bretherton had to vacate these premises to allow for the construction of the first part of New Street railway station and the empty buildings proved ideal for the show. In December 1849 the show was enlarged to include cattle, and was held in temporary buildings erected on vacant land between Kent Street and Pershore Street.

Map of cattle show, 1849.

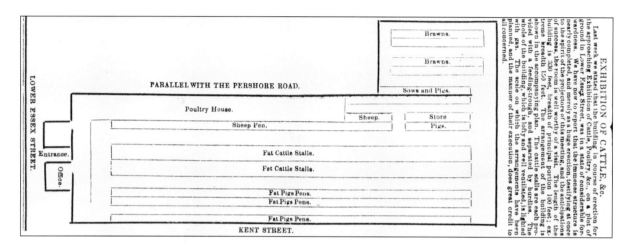

Among the first visitors to Bingley Hall were equestrian events, for which the central compartments were converted into a theatre. William Cooke's 'Colossal Equestrian Establishment' visited the hall from 10 February 1851, when the Hall was fitted up as a Roman amphitheatre. In December 1853 Mr Tonks again arranged for the central part of the hall to be converted for a horse riding event.

There were a number of other public halls in Birmingham that held exhibitions and other events from time to time. The People's Hall, on the corner of Princip Street and Loveday Street, was erected during 1841 at a cost of £2,400, but was little used and ended its days as factory buildings. The building contained several rooms and included a lecture room 50ft square, with a gallery. Its short public existence came to an end in 1849, when the hall was offered for sale. Henry Holder opened a room, in Coleshill Street during 1850, which he called the 'Hall of Nations'. In September 1850 this hall was used to stage a Grand Dahlia Show.

Birmingham businessmen and tradespeople were among the first to form a local committee for what was then called the Great Exhibition of Industry of All Nations, to be held in London during 1851. Formed in March 1850, they took it upon themselves to organise those who wanted to exhibit and the amount of space required. William P. Marshall, who had been secretary for the Birmingham Exposition, was appointed secretary for this committee. The Birmingham and Midland Counties Society was also formed to cater for their members to visit the Great Exhibition. Subscribers paid a fixed weekly amount for admission and railway travel.

In 1865 the complement of public exhibition halls was increased through the building of Curzon Hall, which was named after Lord Curzon, MP for Atherstone. Money for the venture was raised by share subscription. Curzon Hall was built to hold dog shows, but soon was adapted for circuses and other events.

The contract to build the hall was awarded during the summer of 1865 and the building was ready for the 1865 Dog Show in December. The annual Dog Show event had been held since 1859. The first shows had been held at May's Repository in Tennant

Cartoon of Midland Cycle and Motorcar Exhibition, January 1898. (*Birmingham Weekly Mercury*)

Street, and in 1863 and 1864 in temporary buildings erected on the Birmingham Canal Co. Old Wharf. Curzon Hall became the first purpose-built venue for the show. Curzon Hall was also the venue for several trade exhibitions and boxing events. The building continued to be used for the annual Dog Show until the early twentieth century. Curzon Hall was then converted into the West End Cinema and opened its doors for customers for the first showing in 1925.

Another exhibition hall was built in Corporation Street during 1890 as part of a Birmingham Exhibition Hall and Winter Gardens scheme. The promoters had been associated with a successful electrical exhibition and hoped the new hall would become an important exhibition venue. The buildings also incorporated a hotel, and space was allotted for sixteen shops that faced Corporation Street and the Old Square. The Exhibition Hall and Winter Gardens had a limited appeal and within five years had been taken over for other uses.

Bingley Hall and the Town Hall continued to host a variety of public events and trade exhibitions. Bingley Hall was even licensed as a cinema in 1910. Regular cattle shows were held there, as well as frequent electrical, homes and brewery exhibitions. The first show for motorcycles and cars took place there in 1897, and from 1905 a Midland Motor Show was arranged. Bingley Hall was fitted out for a political meeting in September 1909, when Prime Minister Balfour attended to give an important speech.

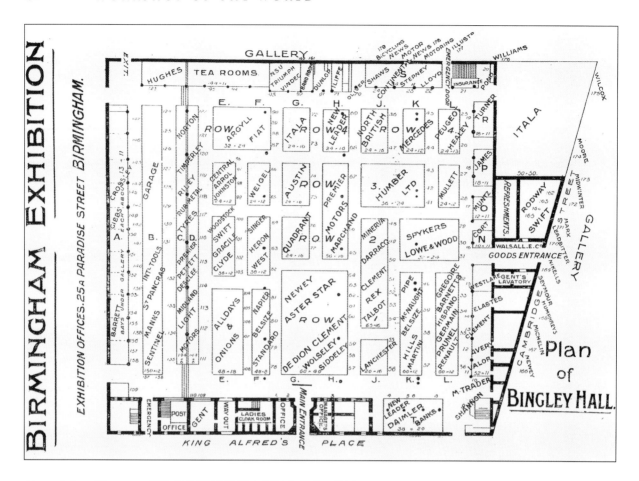

Above: Automobiles, cycles and motor cycles were exhibited together in some of the early shows at Bingley Hall.

Right: The Building Trades exhibition held at Bingley Hall in 1925 featured a Fordson petrol locomotive hauling a pair of skips along a section of 2-ft gauge track. *(Birmingham Post September 1925)*

Outside the meeting, protesters from the Women's Freedom League demonstrated for votes for women.

By 1910 exhibitions were being held across the world, but Britain seemingly lagged behind the great continental trade fairs that were held in Brussels, Lyons, Leipzig, Paris, Prague and the Netherlands. During 1912 the Birmingham Chamber of Commerce investigated the possibilities for holding similar exhibitions in Britain to compete with the great European trade fairs. Birmingham felt that British industries did not receive the recognition and publicity they merited, and it was decided to encourage world interest in the products of the British Empire. The war intervened before the project materialised, but following the cessation of hostilities an arrangement was made with the Board of Trade and the Chamber of Commerce, whereby the heavier products of British industry were to be exhibited.

The Board of Trade had organised the first British Industries Fair in London during 1915, but now plans were made to hold a part of the fair at Castle Bromwich Aerodrome. The site chosen had been built during the war and comprised three permanent aircraft hangars. The industries shown at the Birmingham Section of the fair included hardware, brass foundry, building, heating with gas and electricity, electricity generation, transmission and use, metalwork, quarries, mining and transport. Other sections of the fair were held in London and (for 1920 only) Glasgow.

The first show to be held at Castle Bromwich took place from 23 February to 5 March 1920 and traders attended the show by invitation only. The Birmingham Chamber of Commerce was responsible for organisation of the fair and the booking of exhibitors. The BIF became an annual event held at the Aerodrome, and at other times the site was used by aircraft. The 1923 show was the first at which traders arrived by air

Best & Lloyd's invitation to the first fair at Castle Bromwich, 1920.

BRITISH INDUSTRIES FAIR
CASTLE BROMWICH
BIRMINGHAM

FEBRUARY 23RD TO MARCH 5TH, 1920

BEST & LLOYD LTD. OF BIRMINGHAM
ARE EXHIBITING AT THE ABOVE AND CORDIALLY INVITE YOU TO VISIT THEM THERE. THEIR REPRESENTATIVES IN ATTENDANCE WILL BE PLEASED TO SEE YOU

LIGHTING FITTINGS — STAND NO. 51
MOTOR FITTINGS — STAND NO. 477

N.B.—SHOULD YOU BE COMING TO BIRMINGHAM IT WOULD BE ADVISABLE TO WRITE AT ONCE TO MR. C. STANLEY, CHAMBER OF COMMERCE, NEW STREET, BIRMINGHAM, STATING DATE AND LENGTH OF VISIT. HOTEL OR BOARDING ACCOMODATION WILL THEN BE FOUND FOR YOU

from Manchester and London. The next year, 1924, Imperial Airways inaugurated a commercial service from Croydon to coincide with the opening of the show. The BIF was often the launching pad for new ideas, when firms exhibited the latest products. Braithwaites, from West Bromwich, had on display for the 1925 show a new range of steel houses.

Attendance numbers and exhibitors steadily increased, and enlargements and improvements were made to the fair buildings from time to time. The most notable improvement was during the winter of 1935, when John Ewell Ltd erected an additional roof span. The BIF site covered 57 acres and the buildings were eventually a third of a mile long, and over 400ft wide. The total area under cover exceeded 16 acres. A rail siding owned by the Air Ministry provided access from the LMS Railway to the BIF buildings and to the manure makers Guanogen. During shows the sidings were sometimes used to exhibit railway-related items.

Some 2 million people attended the BIF show in 1939, but organisation for further shows was suspended when war broke out. Castle Bromwich Aerodrome then reverted to military use. Spitfire planes and Lancaster bombers built across the road at the Vickers factory were tested there before being despatched for war use.

Hopes of re-establishing the BIF at Castle Bromwich were expressed as early as 1944, when a fair in 1946 was proposed. However, by 1946 some people thought that the show should not be restarted. Nevertheless, arrangements for a BIF at Castle Bromwich went ahead for 1947. New entrance buildings were erected, and when the show opened attendances by traders and exhibitors were again high. The Birmingham section continued to deal with engineering, hardware, building and mining.

New ideas and developments continued to be features of the show. A commercial helicopter service between Castle Bromwich and London, the first in Europe, marked

British Industries Fair show of 1928: a view of the gas industries section.

British Industries Fair building exterior as seen from the Chester road. *(Heartland Press Collection)*

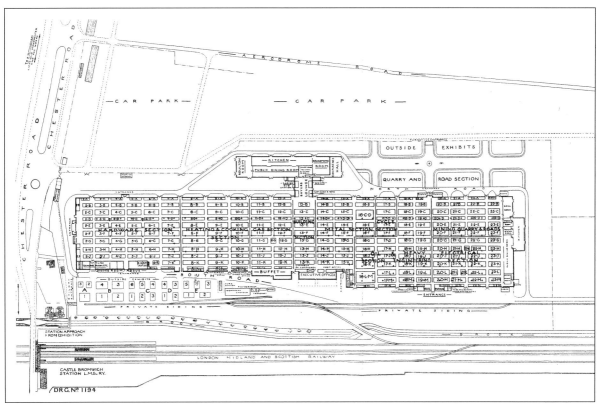

Plan of the British Industries Fair for 1932, showing the outside and inside exhibits. The long open interior was divided into eight sections to cater for the major industries: hardware, heating and cooking, gas, building, metal sections, mining and quarry and roads, oil and heavy engineering, and electrical. *(BIF Catalogue, 1932)*

the opening of the 1949 BIF Show. Meanwhile, improvements continued to be made to the site and the BIF buildings were extended further. However, by the time of the 1955 show the BIF site had become somewhat jaded when compared with other European exhibition halls and the shows held there. One American visitor to the Castle Bromwich Fair stated, 'Either shut up this show, or make it a real one.'

The fair was again held at Castle Bromwich in 1956, but the continued use of the building remained in question. No fair was held in London during 1957, and the BIF buildings were host to the whole fair for the first time. This was the last time that the fair was held in Birmingham. Members of the Federation of British Industry decided, in December 1957, that more specialised trade shows were of more benefit than the general annual trade fair. The BIF buildings were closed down. Flights from the aerodrome ceased in 1958 and the whole site was sold off for housing in 1960, and the BIF buildings lay idle for a while before being demolished to make way for the new Castle Vale Housing Estate. The Birmingham Chamber of Commerce began to work on the concept of a new, purpose-built exhibition centre in Birmingham.

Another exhibition hall, in the heart of Birmingham, was included in the Civic Centre scheme, first proposed during the 1930s. All work on this project was halted during the Second World War, but the Civic Centre development was revived in 1958 and various properties in Bridge Street were purchased during 1959 and 1960 for an updated scheme. Pearce & Cutler's factory in Bridge Street and the Boatman's Chapel on the corner of Bridge Street and Holliday Street were purchased in 1960 with the intention to use the land for a new car park and the exhibition hall. A multi-storey car park was eventually built, but work on the exhibition hall was delayed. Another part of the Civic Centre scheme was the conversion of Gas Street Basin into an ornamental lake. Fortunately, this proposal was not proceeded with, and the canal-side improvements carried out there from 1990 have had a far more beneficial effect for the area.

The number of exhibitions held in Birmingham declined during the 1960s, as if in sympathy with the declining local manufacturing base. Bingley Hall, which was enlarged during the 1950s to give direct access to Broad Street, continued to deal with the existing demand until its closure and demolition in 1984.

Exhibition and conference facilities in Birmingham were transformed during the 1990s when the International Convention Centre (ICC), National Indoor Arena (NIA) and Symphony Hall were constructed. All three were canal-side locations in the centre of Birmingham, and an integral part of the regeneration for this area. The ICC and adjacent Symphony Hall occupy a large strip of land that extends from Centenary Square through to the canal. Part of this site was the old location of Bingley Hall, but also incorporates land once occupied by the Prince of Wales Theatre and William Butler's Crown Brewery. A large amount of spoil and earth was excavated to open out the frontage to the canal. The foundation stone was laid in 1986 beside the canal, and construction work steadily went ahead until 1991. A covered glass walkway separates the ICC from Symphony Hall, which descends to canal level and the bridge link over to Brindley Place.

The ICC specialises in providing conference facilities at Hall 1 and Halls 3 to 11. Symphony Hall (or Hall 2) has gained an international reputation for its acoustics and facilities provided for recitals and other musical performances. Delegates visiting conferences at the ICC and NIA follow the canal towpath that forms the link between the two venues. The NIA was also completed in 1991 and comprises an oval building constructed on the site of a disused timber wharf; it extends over the main railway line between Birmingham and Wolverhampton. The NIA frequently hosts concerts and sporting events and is particularly remembered for the Eurovision Song Contest and G8 Summit that were held there in 1998.

Despite the closure of the British Industry Fair halls at Castle Bromwich, the Birmingham Chamber of Commerce remained keen to promote British industry, and a new scheme for a National Exhibition Centre (NEC) based in the Midlands was proposed. Land was acquired on the boundary between Birmingham and Solihull and close to Elmdon Airport and the main railway line between Birmingham and Coventry. The NEC Group Ltd was formed in 1970 to manage the new Centre and the contract for construction was awarded to R.M. Douglas, building contractors. Work commenced in 1973 after Prime Minister Edward Heath laid the foundation stone, which is visible in the main Piazza.

The first five halls were completed around the central Piazza, with a sixth hall joined to Hall 1. Construction work was completed, on schedule, during October 1975. HM the Queen performed the official opening ceremony on 2 February 1976, which also coincided with the opening of the first show, the International Gift Fair. These halls remain the core of the site. Made to different dimensions, the largest is Hall 5, which has nine vehicle entry (VE) doors in addition to the main entrance. Hall 4 has seven VE doors, while Hall 3 has eight. Hall 3 was divided from the start into two halls, 3 and 3a. Halls 1 and 2 are smaller in size. Hall 1 was joined to the old Hall 6, now the Pavilions, through a covered link-way. Around the halls, car parks were laid out and beside Hall 5 a rectangular strip of land was laid out as an Outside Exhibition Area.

The Pavilions was later linked to the NEC Arena and then to the Forum. Further extensions led to the building of the New Halls, which were arranged around three sides of a central atrium and occupied a larger area than the earlier halls. The first halls on this side were opened during 1989 as Halls 6, 7 and 8, numbered from south to north. Access to these halls from the old side was by footpath. Additional buildings were completed during 1992, creating Halls 9, 10, 11 and 12 as well as a new overhead link-way from the Piazza that was called the Skywalk. The sequence of numbering for the 1989 Halls was reversed at the same time, when Hall 8 became Hall 6 and Hall 6 became Hall 8. Three existing halls on the NEC site thus had the distinction of being numbered 6 at one time or another. Halls 17, 18, 19 and 20 were completed during September 1998. A portion of Bickenhill plantation was cut down to make way for the latest halls and perimeter road.

A herd of deer still live in this wood and are sometimes seen when they graze near the fence. There are plans to fill in the final side of the square with Halls 14 to 16. In the meantime the space is filled by a temporary tent structure known as Hall 16, which was put up in 2000 for the Gardeners' World Show. The Atrium is a vast glass-covered and glass-lined space that affords access to all halls on the New Side. It rises to a dizzy height, in cathedral-like splendour, and must truly be a Birmingham rival to the old Crystal Palace in London. Above the Atrium, facing Halls 6 to 8 is the Gallery, which is a place shielded from the hustle and bustle of the shows and events held below. The NEC Halls are geared up to hold trade exhibitions and public shows such as the Good Food Show, Clothes Show, Motor Show, Commercial Vehicle Show and Antiques for Everyone. Often several shows are held at the same time. The public and trade visitors only see each show during opening hours, but the build-up and break-down procedure is worth recounting.

A large number of people are employed at the NEC to provide services for the exhibitors. These include stand constructors, carpet fitters, catering staff, cleaning staff and security. Every time a show commences another army of people come on site; including the event organisers, the exhibitors, transport drivers and various contractors.

SHOW ORGANISATION AT THE NEC, 2002

Every show begins with an empty and clean hall. NEC staff mark out the floor for stand numbers or other features. All show material arrives by road in large trailers, vans or exhibitors' cars. NEC staff restrict the movements of all vehicles, allowing them down to the halls through the control points at specified times. A network of roadways intersects the site and provides access to all vehicle entry doors. Trailers and vans are also permitted to enter the halls at the discretion of NEC staff. The exhibitors choose what stand material is provided. Some prefer to build up the stands themselves and employ carpenters, stand builders and other contractors for this purpose. On-site services may also perform this work. At times it seems there is a truly continental scene as French, German, Italian and Spanish workers mingle, putting together the varied and unique structures for the show. As time is frequently at a premium these contractors put in long days, working until late in the evening and sometimes through the night.

Melvilles are an important on-site contractor, whose expertise is called on to supply shell schemes, electric wiring and lighting, plumbing, carpets, forklifts, furniture and even plants. The plants are grown at a nearby nursery, near Whitlocks End, owned by Melvilles. Forklift services are an essential part of any show preparation, as they are frequently called upon to lift pallets off trailers and place them on the stands. The major forklift providers on site are TNT Showfreight, Schenkers and Geologistics. Every show build-up and break-down is characterised by the scurrying hither and thither of the forklifts. Cranes are brought in for the heavier lifts, and 'cherry-pickers' also make appearances for the use of the riggers. The riggers' job is perhaps the most precarious, as it they who go up to the roof of the hall to hang drapes and banners. Other staff set up the entrance arrangement, providing booths, barriers and computer equipment.

The show gradually takes shape, and as the hall is filled with stands, vehicles are excluded. Exhibitors with material for their stands must barrow or carry these items to the stands. With the larger shows build-up can occupy a number of days, with designated operations being carried out to a timetable. Public shows often have seating areas where rows are built up in front of, or around, a small arena or stage. A remarkable amount of waste is generated during the build-up, as old pallets, cardboard wire, and plastic packages are thrown aside. ISS cleaners are kept in regular employment, keeping the gangways and doorways clear.

The day before the show sees the main carpet-laying being done. Many shows have carpets laid in all the gangways. The fitters work with remarkable speed, putting down rolls of coloured carpet or tiles. The cleaners then come in at night for the last clean before the opening. Some people work right up to the appointed hour, tidying stands and even bringing in late exhibits. Meanwhile, visitors gather outside the entrance, waiting for the show to open. Some buy tickets for the paid shows, others fill out registration forms for trade admission. Then, at the appointed hour, the organisers give permission for the doors to open or the barriers to be set aside and the people come in. To them this may be a magical world of stands and displays, few realise the work of preparation that goes on beforehand. Some shows are very busy, others less so. The only constant factor is the exhibitors, who are present at every show and considerably swell the numbers of workers present in and around the halls.

On the last day of the show, and particularly during the last hour, proceedings slow down markedly. Every minute seems to last as long as ten. Then the show closes and the contractors move in to dismantle the stands and pack away the exhibits. Things move more rapidly at break-down, and by the next day only shells of the stands remain. Stand fitters methodically take down what had been built up, reclaiming most material for reuse. Carpets are rolled up and carpet tiles carefully stacked. The owners quickly reclaim furniture and hired electrical equipment. Forklifts move throughout the halls again, carrying heavy pallets and equipment back to the trailers. As soon as space becomes available vans and trailers are again permitted to come into the hall to assist the break-down procedure.

When the last vestiges of the stands are removed, all that is left is the rubbish that litters the floor. The cleaners come in, and one drives a forklift with a broom across the forks. As the forklift drives forward, layers of rubbish are pushed to one end of the hall. Some of the cardboard is collected for recycling, and rolls of carpets are picked up by designated charities, but most of the rubbish, which includes plastic, cans, paper, bits of wire and lengths of wood, is loaded by the cleaners into the Onyx Rubbish Carts and driven off-site for landfill. At the end of this operation the hall is left clean for the next show.

The occupiers of the halls can be quite varied. One month the hall might contain motorcars or commercial vehicles. In the course of a few months there might be a succession of boats, caravans, furniture or machinery. The International Gift Fair was renamed as the Spring Fair, and this remains a regular event, held each February. It is one of the few events that is capable of occupying the whole site. Some shows and events also use the Outside Exhibition Area by Hall 5, or adjacent car parks. During the Horse of the Year Show much of the South Car Park is given over for stable accommodation and restricted access ways to the Forum, Arena and Pavillions where the show is held.

Occasionally some of the outer car parks have been adapted as venues for specific events. The car park area is extensive, almost completely surrounding the halls. Roads and footpaths cross this area, providing access to the halls. So large is the area covered by these parks that some portions have been sold off for hotels and other developments. Parts of the South Car Park were used to build the Crown Plaza Hotel, while in 2005 a section of the West Car Park was reserved for a new office development.

An important achievement was the NEC Group's successful bid to hold the International Textile Machinery Association Show in Birmingham in 2003. Known as ITMA, this show brought visitors from all over the world.

ITMA, 2003

The NEC was privileged to have held the International Textile Machinery Association Show in 2003, an event held every four years, but which had never been to the UK. All halls, with the exception of the Arena, were used for the show, one of the biggest trade shows to be held at the NEC. Other shows of comparable size are the annual Spring Fair and the Furniture Show.

ITMA was a truly global event, drawing on exhibitors worldwide and playing host to an expected 100,000 visitors. For Andy Bird and his team, organisation was a tremendous challenge, although it proved to be one easily overcome and enhanced the reputation of the NEC for its ability to hold exhibitions of this size.

Cematex were the organisers for the exhibition. For the British show two new product sectors were launched. These were dyestuff and chemicals, and associated goods and services. The halls were transformed into a giant textile plant. Machinery was brought in, assembled and put into working order. Transport was an organiser's nightmare. Exhibits arrived by road in vans, lorries, and 'forty-footers' or articulated paired wagons. All loads were booked in to the site and regulated by Panalpina. Motor units and 40ft trailer combinations transported a significant proportion of the machinery. Loads from the European textile makers arrived daily, with trailers packed with components and parts. Some travelled the length of Europe with loads from Italy and Turkey. Other cargoes arrived by sea as container loads, which were transferred to the 40ft trailers at the ports to make the final leg by road. Certain parts of the NEC site around the halls were designated as container parks for the off-loading and storage of containers. Many heavy lifting cranes and a large fleet of forklift trucks were kept busy with unloading vehicles, both inside and outside the hall.

The build-up for the show began on 30 September 2003. Halls 1 to 3 and part of Hall 4 were dedicated to spinning, the rest of Hall 4 held a non-woven section. Hall 5 was devoted to knitting and Halls 9 to 12 held weaving machinery. In Hall 8 was the dyestuffs section, while Halls, 6, 7 and 16 to 20 were dyeing and finishing. Storage areas were provided in the Forum and Pavillions, leaving only the Arena available for concerts. A circular bus route was provided daily around the site for the use of contractors and exhibitors.

The Weaving Halls held large machines used in the weaving of yarn and thread. These machines arrived early to enable operators to thread the spindles and test the machines. Machinery on show throughout the halls was very varied and included cotton spinning systems; worsted, semi-worsted or woollen spinning; yarn steaming; texturing, bulking and crimping machines; twisting machines; cordage and rope making machines for web formation; bonding of non-wovens and felting; weaving machinery; knitting and hosiery; and washing, bleaching, dyeing and printing.

Each hall was unique. At one end of the site was Hall 17 where dyeing and finishing machines were on show. This was a multi-cultural hall, with stands from Austria, Britain, Canada, China, Ireland, Italy, Japan, the Netherlands, Thailand, Turkey and the USA included.

Textile production has gradually transferred to the Far East, and firms like Kidd & Zigrino based at Nakorn Pathom, Thailand are examples of the trade that has developed in this part of the world during the last twenty years. Kidd & Zigrino were based in Buxton, Derbyshire, but had moved out to Thailand to take advantage of cheaper workforce and building costs. K. & Z. Corporation Ltd supply a range of printing and chemical and dye preparation equipment, which include flat screen printing tables used for printing T-shirts and polo shirts.

European textile producers were still represented by a host of makers, especially from Italy. The firm of Noseda based at Ta/rerio, Como, had a large stand near the front entrance of Hall 17, which had a range of textile dyeing machines on show. Standardisation throughout the industry has led yarn makers to produce yarn in certain sizes that are wrapped around cones ready for dyeing and washing. Noseda had a robot on display that stacked and restacked cones on spindles prior to their passage into the body of the yarn treatment machine. The many variations in fabric led to the development of machines for dyeing, washing and after-printing washing. Machines were also developed for dyeing fabrics in rope form. Rope-dyeing machines were to be found in both Hall 17 and 18 and comprised long, broad cylinders where the textiles were treated at atmospheric pressure or other pressures and temperatures.

ITMA was open to visitors at the NEC from 22 to 29 October 2003. The show then closed and the process of dismantling the stands continued until 6 November.

All industries are represented at one time or another, and visitors come to the NEC from all parts of the globe. During the nineteenth and twentieth centuries Birmingham factories were the workshop to the world. In the first years of the twenty-first century the NEC became the Shop Window to the World.

Unfortunately, this achievement appears now all too brief. ITMA proved the peak. Trade shows are diminishing in size, and competition with an increasing number of other exhibition centres is taking its toll. The summer of 2004 was the last time the Motor Show was booked for the NEC. Dwindling attendances at the Motor Show was a contributory factor influencing the relocation of this prestigious show to London for 2006.

The 4×4 garage outside Hall 3 during the final Motor Show held at the NEC, 2004. *(Heartland Press Collection)*

The last Motor Show at the NEC took place in May 2004. A number of new features were included to increase appeal for the general public. Among these were the introduction of a 4×4 off-road course through the woods that lie to the side of Halls 6, 20, 19, 18 and 17. *(Heartland Press Collection)*

Below: Part of the off-road course. *(Heartland Press Collection)*

In an attempt to improve its image, an extensive makeover for the Piazza was planned. During the summer of 2005 contractors Laing O'Rourke moved into Hall 2 and embarked on the refurbishment of the Piazza. Anyone passing through the Piazza during June, July and August frequently met a cloud of dust as the work went ahead. The makeover was accompanied with a series of name changes, as suites were rebranded. Perhaps the saddest loss was the renaming of the Lucas Centre, severing another link with that once proud firm.

Thus the exhibition trade goes on and planners continue to lay out future shows, these now being biased to the public shows and events. Such is the present world that lives for change, and retail and sales have become the backbone of society. Regrettably, it is at the expense of manufacturing, and time will only tell whether this is really the best way forward.

CONCLUSION

Throughout Britain, manufacturing industry has been subject to considerable change in the last 300 years. At the start of the eighteenth century the common form of industrial power was the water mill or windmill. Water power was particularly well used where stream and river courses were frequently altered to feed a mill pool, and the head of water that built up was used to drive a water wheel. Where water was fast flowing some mills had wheels by the main stream. With the advent of the steam engine and the development of power to turn wheels and rollers, manufacturing moved from the waterside to the factory.

It was at James Pickard's mill in Water Street, Birmingham, that the first steam engine was used to turn a mill. Pickard's invention has been criticised by some historians who doubted his ability to produce the engine. One author even suggested that he had stolen the idea from James Watt. More enlightened accounts have accepted Pickard's role in the development of the crank, which was so important in the development of engines for rolling metal and grinding corn. Pickard belonged to an ever-increasing list of people who, through innovation and skill, have made important contributions to the development of technology and industry throughout the world.

Birmingham people have shown a remarkable ability to adapt to new trades and skills. Some proved less successful than others. John Wyatt pioneered mechanical cotton spinning in the town long before Richard Arkwright perfected his method at Cromford. But it is Arkwright who is best remembered for his invention, rather than Wyatt. Cotton spinning was later carried on at Robinson Archer's Steam Mill in Fazeley Street, where wick yarn was produced during the last decade of the eighteenth century.

Cotton spinning never became an important local trade. In Birmingham trade was dominated by the working of metals. Out of this base grew the multitude of different trades for which Birmingham became famous. The trades chosen for *Workshop of the World* are intended to complement the subjects dealt with in *Birmingham's Industrial Heritage*, 2002. This first volume concentrated on industries that were prominent in the twentieth century. The second examines industries that developed in the eighteenth and nineteenth centuries. Some were the bedrock of manufacturing in the town, providing the means of employment for a growing population and contributing to the success of the city. Birmingham manufacturers supplied the world, despatching engines, equipment, machines and tools to many parts.

An important aim of both *Birmingham's Industrial Heritage* and *Workshop of the World* was to discuss methods of manufacture and to show transition as firms adapted to new requirements. With some industries, such as the making of jewellery and glass making, traditional skills were retained, but with other trades, through competition, there was a general desire to improve. This was especially true of firms that made a common product. Castings, forgings and presswork items were produced by a host of firms as part of the supply chain for the makers of guns, sewing machines, cycles and cars. These same skills were as easily applied to the repetitive moulding machines that churned out plastic parts. Fashion also played a part, particularly with the metallic bedstead trade in which

Birmingham excelled. Public demand changed to a desire for wooden bedsteads and bedroom furniture. The change left the bedstead firms either to make other products or transfer to wooden bedstead making. Change, in fact, became the very core of local industry.

Through skill and innovation new ideas and trades found funds, investment and support to develop, and a skilled local workforce provided the means to produce the goods. The whole process is encapsulated in one word, 'forward'. It appears on the coat of arms of the city and is a single statement for both the lives and work of Birmingham people. It is symbolic of their intentions and hopes. And in the words of Birmingham songwriter Laurie Hornsby, his song 'Birmingham' ends with 'Forward goes Birmingham'. So business and industry still go forward, to meet the challenges and demands of the twenty-first century.

SOURCES

LOCAL NEWSPAPERS

Aris's Birmingham Gazette (*Birmingham Gazette*, *Birmingham Daily Gazette*)
Aston Chronicle
Aston News
Aston Times
Birmingham Commercial Herald
Birmingham Daily Post
Birmingham Echo
Birmingham Evening Despatch
Birmingham Journal
Birmingham Weekly Mercury
Birmingham Weekly Post
Harborne Herald
The Sketch
Sunday Mercury
Weekly Mercury

OTHER PERIODICALS

Birmingham Gas Department Magazine
Birmingham Gazette
Birmingham Magazine of Arts and Industries (1897–1904)
British Clayworker
City Chimes & Birmingham Financial News (1896–1899)
Empire Mail and Overseas Trade (February 1926)
Engineer
Furniture Gazette
Gas Journal
Gaskell & Chambers Magazine
Gentleman's Journal and Gentlewoman's Court Review
GKN Magazine
Illustrated Journal of the Patents Office
Journal of Gas Lighting
Kynoch Journal
Lucas Reflections
The Metal Journal
Mining Journal
Review of Commerce (1913 and 1914)
Sport & Play
Tinsley Magazine (1889)
Trade Marks Journal

TRADE DIRECTORIES

Kelly's Directory (various dates)
Ryland's Trade Directory
West's Warwickshire Directory (1830)

CITY OF BIRMINGHAM GAS DEPARTMENT DESCRIPTIVE BOOKLETS ON GAS WORKS

Adderley Street (1928)
Nechells Works (1923)
Nechells Laboratories and Coal Test Works (1928)
Saltley Works (1923)
Windsor Street Works (1923)

BOOKS AND PAMPHLETS

Birmingham Tells the World, Empire Trade League, 1932
A Century of Achievement: The Story of Laughton & Sons Ltd, 1860–1960, York, William Sessions Ltd, 1960
Dent, R.K, *Trades and manufactures of Birmingham*, 1897
The House of Holden: A Century of Progress and Development, 1932
Prosser, R.B., *Birmingham Inventors and Inventions*, 1881, reprinted Wakefield, S.R. Publishers, 1977
Proud Occasion, Birmingham, Birmingham, Thornley & Knight Ltd, 1947
Visitors' Handbook to Birmingham, Birmingham, Cornish Brothers, 1854

Birmingham & Alphabetical arranged guide to the Industrial Resources of the Midland Metropolis (BRL 103286)

INDEX